# TRAVEL TIME FOR KIDS

# Monster puzzles

© 2007 Autumn Publishing

Published in 2007 by Autumn Publishing, Chichester, West Sussex, UK PO20 7EQ.

Printed in Malaysia

Cover illustration by Ken Gamage

7+

"Don't forget to pull out and display your best pages!"

ISBN 978 1 84531 668 6

# Hide and seek

Twenty dragons are hiding in the trees. Find and circle them if you please.

# Countries **word** puzzle

There are eight countries hidden in this grid.
Circle the words as you find them.

```
C A N A D A R T E
H Z W M L D C O N
I N D I A R H N G
N K A S O A I P L
A H S R X M L I A
C V Y A N K E D N
G R E E C E E S D
P E K L J T L F I
D C S E Q U H P M
H O L L A N D R U
```

# Hidden word

Cross out the letters that appear twice in the grid.
The letters that are left spell the name of a country.
Write your answer on the line below.

_____

| B | H | E | U | L |
|---|---|---|---|---|
| O | D | W | N | A |
| G | N | D | Y | W |
| A | Q | U | H | P |
| L | O | T | Q | B |

# Wheel of **mystery**

This secret code wheel will help you to break the codes shown
on the next four pages.

# Whispers

Using the secret code wheel, crack the code to find out where the children are going to meet.

# Secret fashions

Look at the coded words in the grid; they read across and down.
When you have cracked the codes, write the words on the lines.

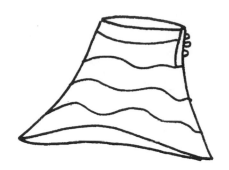

_____

_____

| a | x | k | a | w | l | o | d | e | t |
|---|---|---|---|---|---|---|---|---|---|
| g | r | y | n | m | b | a | v | z | w |
| | | | b | | d | l | j | y | s |
| r | w | a | a | | p | r | | l | p |
| e | f | s | a | | m | u | | i | k |
| d | j | k | e | | s | a | | x | c |
| e | g | m | q | | t | h | | k | p |
| | | | | | u | i | | f | w |
| p | h | u | q | s | d | t | y | o | p |

_____

_____

8

# Crossword in code

Look at the coded words in the crossword grid.
When you have cracked the codes, write the words on the lines.

# Coded sports

The words for the sports are written in code at the bottom of the page. Crack the code, then draw lines to join the sports to the boxes.

# **Question** time

How many ribs does a human have?

a) 12 ☐
b) 18 ☐
c) 24 ☐
d) 32 ☐

# Puzzles for 4

Complete the grids by filling in the missing numbers.

**1**

| 12 | + | 4 | = |  |
|----|----|----|----|----|
| − | ■ | + | ■ | − |
| 10 | − |  | = | 8 |
| = | ■ | = | ■ | = |
| 2 | + | 6 | = |  |

**2**

|  | + | 11 | = | 16 |
|----|----|----|----|----|
| + | ■ | + | ■ | + |
| 6 | + |  | = | 9 |
| = | ■ | = | ■ | = |
| 11 | + | 14 | = |  |

**3**

|  | + | 9 | = | 13 |
|----|----|----|----|----|
| + | ■ | − | ■ | + |
| 10 | − |  | = | 7 |
| = | ■ | = | ■ | = |
| 14 | + | 6 | = |  |

**4**

| 3 | × |  | = | 12 |
|----|----|----|----|----|
| × | ■ | × | ■ | × |
| 3 | × | 2 | = |  |
| = | ■ | = | ■ | = |
|  | × | 8 | = | 72 |

# Fairy tale maze

Starting at number 1, connect the dots to complete the maze.
Help Glenda find her way to the cauldron.

# Space watch

Trace the lines, then use crayons to finish the picture.

# Word trail

Use the picture clues to fill in the word trail.
The last letter of each word is the first of the next word.

# Look and match

Look carefully at these signs. Which pictures do you think they go with? Draw lines to connect the signs to the pictures.

# Creepy maze

Help the wizard through the creepy maze to his house.

# Different-sized **dragons**

The words SHORT and TALL appear across, up, and down
16 times in the puzzle below. Shade the squares.

| T | A | L | L | T | S | H | O | R | T | A |
|---|---|---|---|---|---|---|---|---|---|---|
| A | L | A | T | T | H | O | R | T | A | L |
| L | O | L | S | H | O | R | T | O | L | L |
| L | H | L | H | O | R | T | A | L | L | L |
| T | S | H | O | R | T | A | L | L | L | L |
| A | H | S | R | O | A | L | L | T | S | S |
| L | O | H | T | A | L | L | L | T | A | H |
| T | R | O | T | S | L | L | A | L | O |
| A | T | R | A | H | O | L | L | L | L | R |

# Grids galore

Complete the grids by filling in the missing numbers.

**1**

| 5 | + | 6 | = | |
|---|---|---|---|---|
| + | ■ | − | ■ | + |
| 4 | − | | = | 1 |
| = | ■ | = | ■ | = |
| | + | 3 | = | |

**2**

| 8 | + | | = | 10 |
|---|---|---|---|---|
| + | ■ | − | ■ | + |
| | − | 0 | = | 7 |
| = | ■ | = | ■ | = |
| | + | 2 | = | |

**3**

| | + | 4 | = | 8 |
|---|---|---|---|---|
| − | ■ | ÷ | ■ | − |
| 2 | × | | = | |
| = | ■ | = | ■ | = |
| | + | 2 | = | |

**4**

| | − | 13 | = | 1 |
|---|---|---|---|---|
| + | ■ | + | ■ | + |
| 8 | − | | = | 3 |
| = | ■ | = | ■ | = |
| | − | 18 | = | 4 |

# Witch shadow?

Winnie the witch is looking for her shadow.
Draw a line to match Winnie to the
correct one.

# Blaze a **trail maze**

Guide Hutch through the maze back to Earth.

# Mysterious message

Look carefully at this message. Can you read it?
Write the message on the pad.

# For your eyes only

This is good for sending a really secret message. You will need a small white candle and some paper. Use the candle to write your message on a piece of paper and give it to a friend. To read the message, your friend just rubs a felt-tip pen over it, or a paintbrush dipped in paint, and the letters will magically appear.

# Hidden **rabbits**

Can you find six baby rabbits hidden in this picture?
They are hiding from their mother.

# Quiz time

What does a dog use to regulate its body temperature?

a) a fan ☐
b) its tongue ☐
c) its nose ☐
d) ice cubes ☐

# Pointing puzzle

Each arrow points to something found in the puzzle below.
Circle these words as you find them.

D S P O T K I N G I
S W O R D N F E R N
G B I A G A O A F R
C T D R A G O N V A
B O E M N H T A I L
H E L M E T F I N F
I D R A E F U R N Y

# **Size** wise

Unscramble these words. They are all **size** words.
Circle these words as you find them.

LALSM  GIB  UGEH

TILTEL  IYTN  IATGN

SVIMASE  ORTSH

LALT  RETAG

# Jungle numbers

Complete the grids by filling in the missing numbers.

**1**

| 3 | + |  | = | 12 |
|---|---|---|---|---|
| × | ■ | × | ■ | ÷ |
|  | ÷ | 2 | = | 6 |
| = | ■ | = | ■ | = |
| 36 | ÷ |  | = | 2 |

**2**

| 2 | × | 6 | = |  |
|---|---|---|---|---|
| + | ■ | − | ■ | − |
|  | − | 1 | = | 2 |
| = | ■ | = | ■ | = |
| 5 | + |  | = | 10 |

**3**

| 15 | ÷ | 3 | = |  |
|---|---|---|---|---|
| − | ■ | × | ■ | + |
| 3 | − | 2 | = |  |
| = | ■ | = | ■ | = |
|  | − | 6 | = | 6 |

**4**

|  | − | 16 | = | 3 |
|---|---|---|---|---|
| + | ■ | − | ■ | + |
| 2 | + |  | = | 14 |
| = | ■ | = | ■ | = |
| 21 | − | 4 | = |  |

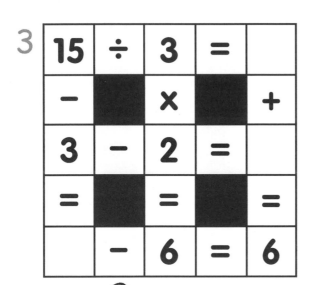

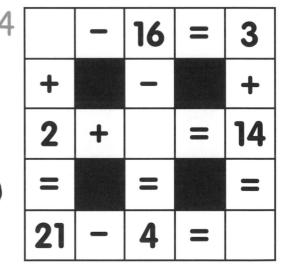

# Dragon dot-to-dot

Starting with number 1, connect the dots to complete the picture.

# Down on **the farm**

Trace the lines, then use crayons to finish the picture.

# What's gone wrong?

The artist has drawn some silly things in this picture.
Can you find them?

# Questions and answers

The answers to these questions can be found in the boxes.
Draw lines to match the questions to the answers.

1. What has branches and a trunk?

2. What do nettles do?

3. Where do pigs live?

4. What do you use to row a boat?

5. What do hens lay?

| eggs |
| --- |
| oars |
| tree |
| sting |
| sty |

# Mossy maze

Find your way from the house to the shed.

# Pyramid puzzler

Starting at number 1, connect the dots to reveal the maze.
Guide the explorer to the top of the pyramid.

# Helicopter **numbers**

Do the problems, then write the answers as words
to complete the crossword.

**a** → 4 + 3 =        **b**  16 ÷ 8 =        **d**  6 − 6 =        **f**  7 + 4 =

**a** ↓ 8 × 2 =        **c**  5 + 3 =        **e**  10 ÷ 10 =

# Quiz time

What is used to make pencils?

a) graphite ☐
b) copper ☐
c) platinum ☐
d) salt ☐

# Crossed swords and words

Work out this puzzle using the things you see below.
Use the words from the puzzle to complete the question.

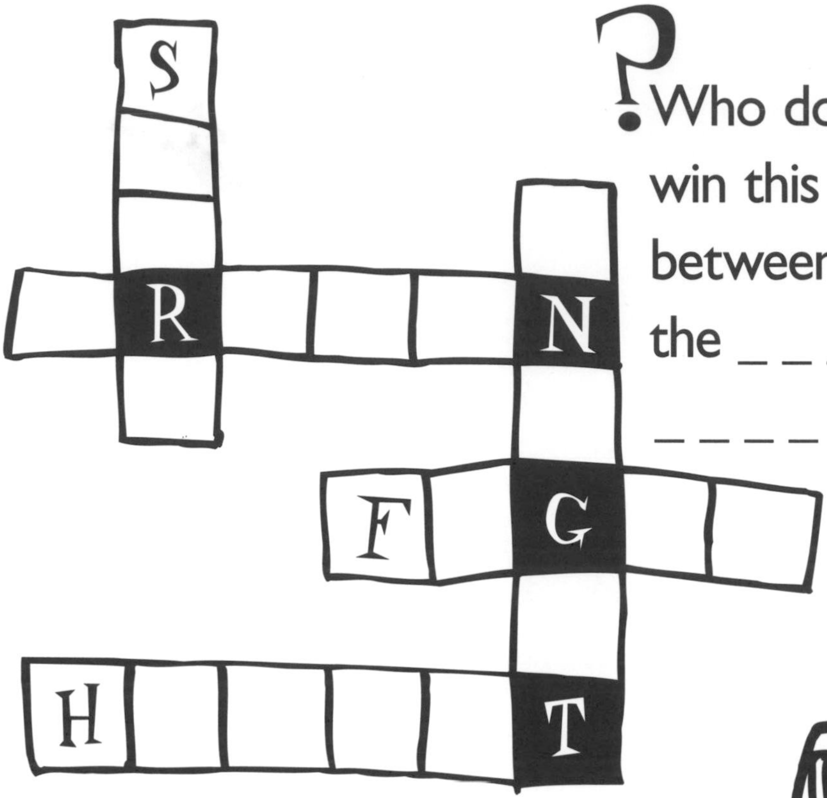

? Who do you think will
win this _ _ _ _ _  _ _ _ _ _
between the _ _ _ _ _ _ with
the _ _ _ _ _ _ and the
_ _ _ _ _ _ ?

# Dragon scale **trail**

Find your way through this scaly maze.

# Creepy code

Using the creepy code on this page, work out Walter the wizard's shopping list on the next page.

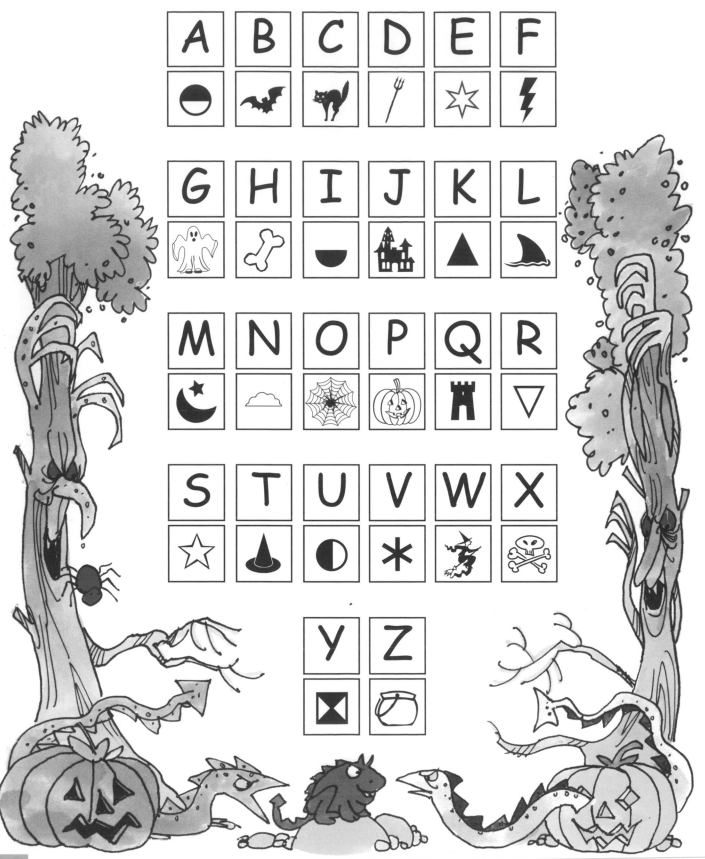

# Walter's shopping list

Follow the code and write the letters in the boxes.
What does Walter need to buy?

# Crack the code

Can you crack this letter code?
Write the answers on the lines.

WEAR EGOI NGTO THEC IRCU STON IGHT.

_____

MYFA MILY ISGO INGO NAPLANE TOMO RROW.

_____

TH EW EA TH ER IS VE RY CO LD TO DA Y.

_____

# **Code** continued!

WOU LDY OUL IKE SOM ECH OCO LAT ECA KE?

MEE TME ATT HEI CER INK THI SAF TER NOO N.

W E WI LL WI NT HE CU PT HI SS EA SO N!

# Busy number bees

Complete the grids by filling in the missing numbers.

**1**

| 7 | − | 6 | = | |
|---|---|---|---|---|
| + | ■ | − | ■ | + |
| 1 | + | | = | 3 |
| = | ■ | = | ■ | = |
| 8 | − | 4 | = | |

**2**

| 7 | + | 4 | = | |
|---|---|---|---|---|
| × | ■ | − | ■ | + |
| 3 | × | | = | 9 |
| = | ■ | = | ■ | = |
| 21 | − | 1 | = | |

**3**

| 12 | + | 3 | = | |
|---|---|---|---|---|
| − | ■ | × | ■ | ÷ |
| | − | | = | 5 |
| = | ■ | = | ■ | = |
| 6 | − | | = | 3 |

**4**

| | + | 9 | = | 13 |
|---|---|---|---|---|
| + | ■ | − | ■ | + |
| 10 | − | | = | 7 |
| = | ■ | = | ■ | = |
| 14 | + | 6 | = | |

# Quiz time

Which bird was called the **peacock of the Indies** when it was first discovered?

a) eagle ☐
b) chicken ☐
c) turkey ☐
d) dodo ☐

# Change of **code**

Use this code to work out the messages on the next four pages.

# Which way?

The country names on this signpost are in code. Can you work out what they are so that the people can find their way? Write the answers in the boxes at the bottom of the page.

# Animal spies

Use the code to crack the names of some of the animals and write them in the boxes.

# Four seasons

Look carefully at the pictures. See if you can crack the codes to find out what happens in the four seasons.
Write the names of the seasons next to the scenes.

# Knights alike

Find the three identical knights.

# Blowing bubbles

Complete the grids by filling in the missing numbers.

**1**

| 12 | + | 4 | = | |
|----|----|----|----|----|
| − | | + | | − |
| 10 | − | | = | 8 |
| = | | = | | = |
| 2 | + | 6 | = | |

**2**

| 2 | + | | = | 10 |
|----|----|----|----|----|
| − | | − | | − |
| | + | 2 | = | 3 |
| = | | = | | = |
| 1 | + | 6 | = | |

( 8 )

**3**

| | + | 11 | = | 16 |
|----|----|----|----|----|
| + | | + | | + |
| 6 | + | | = | 9 |
| = | | = | | = |
| 11 | + | 14 | = | |

**4**

| 3 | + | 6 | = | |
|----|----|----|----|----|
| + | | − | | − |
| 2 | + | | = | 6 |
| = | | = | | = |
| | − | 2 | = | 3 |

( 3 )

( 7 )

# **Mirror** mysteries

Here is the alphabet in mirror writing.
Put a mirror along the dotted line to read the letters.

What does this message in mirror writing say?

WRITE YOUR NAME HERE

# Wizard fireworks

Use crayons to finish this picture.

# Giant maze

Show Jack the way through the maze to the bottom of the beanstalk.

# Quiz time

Which swimming stroke is named after an insect?

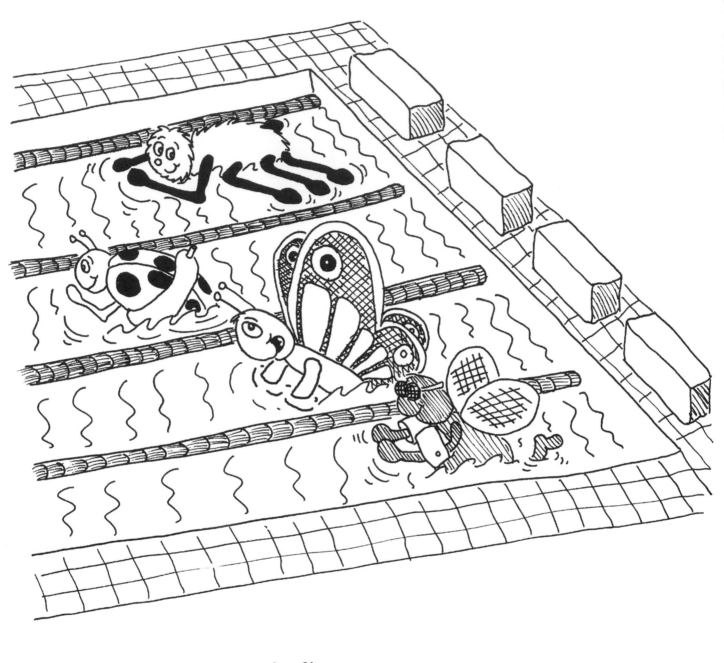

a) fly ☐
b) crawl ☐
c) butterfly ☐
d) beetle ☐

# Quiz time

In Morse code, which letter is shown by a single dot or flash?

a) z  ☐
b) s  ☐
c) a  ☐
d) e  ☐

# Dragon breath

Work your way through this smoky maze.

Start

Finish

# Hidden word

Cross out the letters that appear twice in the grid. Reading from top to bottom, the letters that are left spell a girl's name.
Write your answer on the line below.

| | | | | |
|---|---|---|---|---|
| W | J | T | O | Z |
| G | B | P | U | F |
| L | Y | G | B | Y |
| O | Z | F | N | I |
| P | N | A | T | W |

_____

# What's the **difference**?

There are 14 differences between these two pictures.
Can you find them?

# Party time!

Finish these dot-to-dot puzzles to complete this picture.

# Messy **work**

Do the problems, then write the answers as words
to complete the crossword.

**a** $4 \times 2 =$      **c** → $9 + 5 =$      **d** $20 \div 10 =$

**b** $20 \div 4 =$      **c** ↓ $20 \times 2 =$      **e** $7 + 3 =$

# Quiz time

Which units are used to measure a horse?

a) arms ☐
b) hands ☐
c) legs ☐
d) fingers ☐

# Wizard **word puzzle**

Look in the grid for eight things that
appear in the picture. You will find the
words by reading across or down.
Circle the words as you find them.

```
C A U L D R O N B
A D V P Z E X V R
N J S Q S C L C O
D S K W A N D O O
L N U M H F L B M
E R L V Y K J W S
R Y L B G I O E T
L G F L Q H G B I
P U M P K I N K C
B X Y N R B O O K
```

# Spell book

There are 8 differences between these two pictures.
Can you find them?

# Global codes

Crack the code on page 50 to work out the names of these six places.
The pictures are clues.

# Surprise!

Starting at number 1, connect the dots to complete the maze.
Help the boy find his way to the hidden surprises!

# Circus maze

Starting at number 1, connect the dots to complete the maze.
Help Barry Bigtop find the clowns.

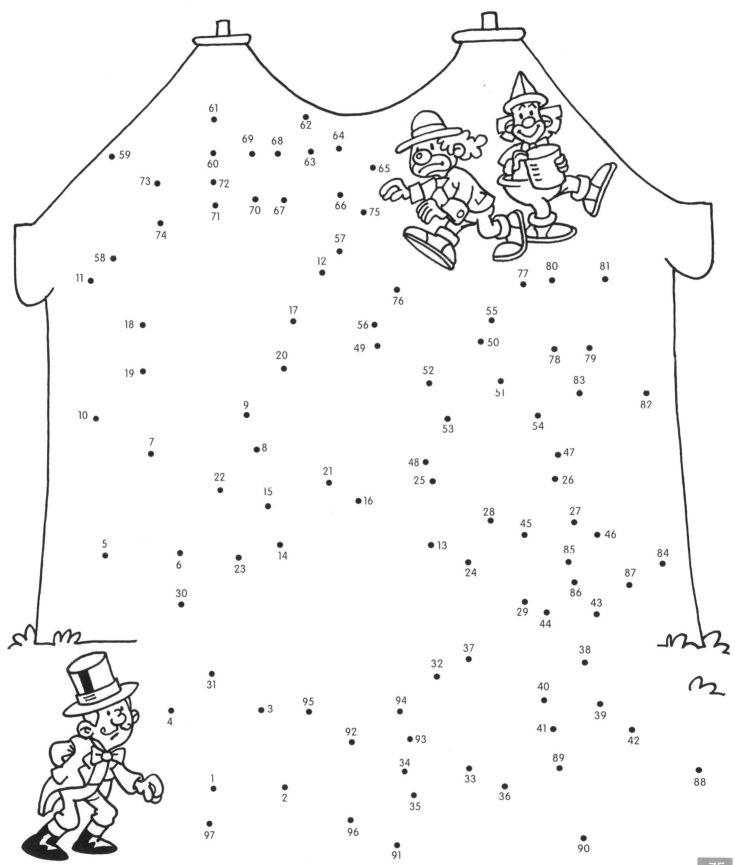

# Underwater problems

Complete the grids by filling in the missing numbers.

**1**

| 6 | − |   | = | 5 |
|---|---|---|---|---|
| + | ■ | × | ■ | + |
| 2 | × |   | = |   |
| = | ■ | = | ■ | = |
| 8 | − | 1 | = | 7 |

**2**

|   | × | 2 | = | 6 |
|---|---|---|---|---|
| + | ■ | − | ■ | − |
| 1 | × |   | = |   |
| = | ■ | = | ■ | = |
| 4 | + |   | = | 5 |

**3**

| 5 | − |   | = | 2 |
|---|---|---|---|---|
| + | ■ | ÷ | ■ | + |
|   | × | 3 | = |   |
| = | ■ | = | ■ | = |
|   | + | 1 | = | 8 |

**4**

| 4 | + |   | = | 6 |
|---|---|---|---|---|
| × | ■ | − | ■ | + |
|   | + | 1 | = |   |
| = | ■ | = | ■ | = |
| 8 | + | 1 | = |   |

76

# Quiz time

What is a female deer called?

a) a doe ☐
b) Mary ☐
c) a stag ☐
d) a foal ☐

# Crazy camping

It's a great night for camping and roasting marshmallows.
Circle the things you might need.

# Morse code

Morse code can be used by flashing a torch or by tapping messages in long or short taps. Years ago, special machines sent Morse code messages on radio waves, but you could just tap a pencil on a table to send a message.

| a | b | c | d | e | f | g | h | i | j | k |
|---|---|---|---|---|---|---|---|---|---|---|
| ·− | −··· | −·−· | −·· | · | ··−· | −−· | ···· | ·· | ·−−− | −·− |
| l | m | n | o | p | q | r | s | t | u | v |
| ·−·· | −− | −· | −−− | ·−−· | −−·− | ·−· | ··· | − | ··− | ···− |
| w | x | y | z | | | | | | | |
| ·−− | −··− | −·−− | −−·· | | | | | | | |

A well-known Morse code message is ···/−−−/···
Do you know what it means?

You can send a message with a torch by Morse code, using long and short flashes.

Send a message to your friend.

# Number creatures

Complete the grids by filling in the missing numbers.

1

| 4 | × | 4 | = |   |
|---|---|---|---|---|
| ÷ | ■ | ÷ | ■ | ÷ |
| 2 | × |   | = | 8 |
| = | ■ | = | ■ | = |
|   | × | 1 | = | 2 |

2

| 4 | + |   | = | 16 |
|---|---|---|---|----|
| + | ■ | + | ■ | − |
|   | − | 2 | = |   |
| = | ■ | = | ■ | = |
| 18 | − |   | = | 4 |

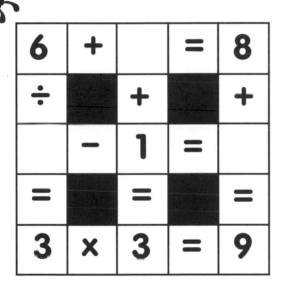

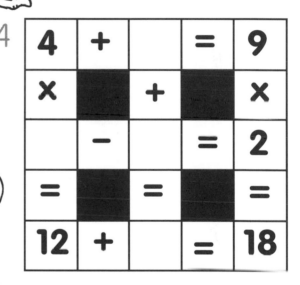

3

| 6 | + |   | = | 8 |
|---|---|---|---|---|
| ÷ | ■ | + | ■ | + |
|   | − | 1 | = |   |
| = | ■ | = | ■ | = |
| 3 | × | 3 | = | 9 |

4

| 4 | + |   | = | 9 |
|---|---|---|---|---|
| × | ■ | + | ■ | × |
|   | − |   | = | 2 |
| = | ■ | = | ■ | = |
| 12 | + |   | = | 18 |

# Which pet?

Follow the leads to find out who has which pet.

# Creepy crossword

The pictures are clues and the numbers beside them
show where each word goes in the grid.

# Daisy maze

These girls have stayed too late making daisy chains, and they want to get home before it gets dark. Can you guide them through the maze?

# Mirror maze

Starting at number 1, connect the dots to complete the maze.
Help Miss Prettypie find her bag.

# Quiz time

What is the only bird that can hover in the air and fly backward?

a) a hummingbird ☐
b) an eagle ☐
c) a sparrow ☐
d) a chicken ☐

# Semaphore

Semaphore is a way of sending messages to someone who is too far away to shout to. Flags or arm signals are used for semaphore.

What do you think this message says?

# Skatepark action

Trace the lines, then use crayons to finish the picture.

# Hocus pocus!

Use the grid to help you draw the picture, copying square by square.

# Seeing stars

Count the stars on each hat and write the numbers in the boxes.
Which hat has the fewest stars?

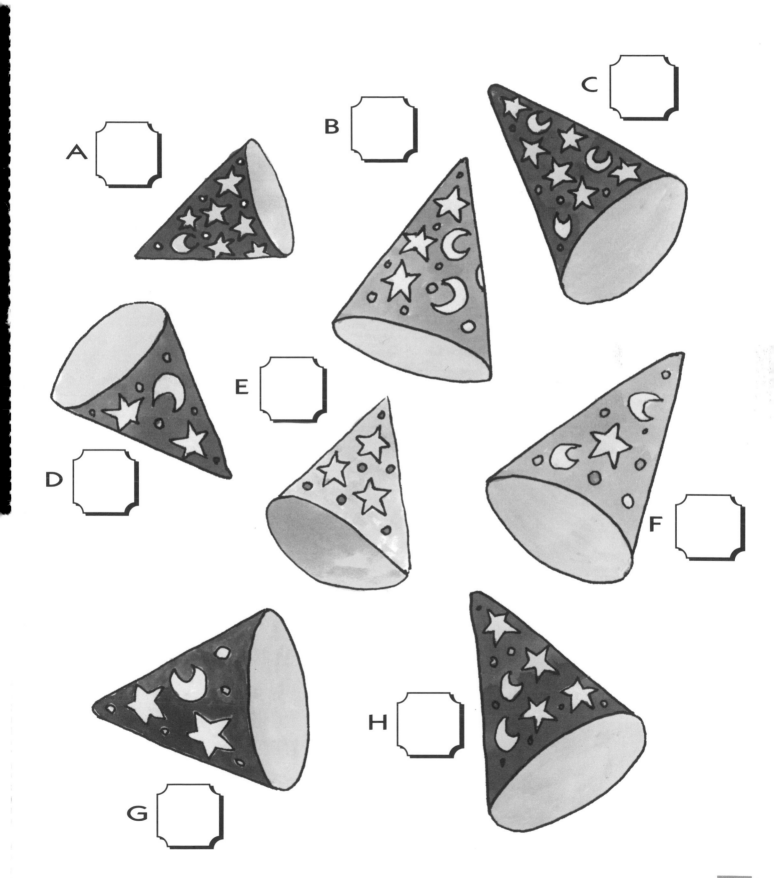

# Shipwrecked **numbers**

Look in the grid for the answers to these problems.

9 x 9 =          2 x 3 =          4 x 1 =

50 − 33 =          6 + 10 =          140 − 110 =

21 ÷ 7 =          100 ÷ 10 =

E I G H T Y O N E
S U C S G D P R S
I Q T H I R T Y E
X F O U R N B T V
T H V C T E N H E
E J E K Y I L R N
E P N J S T M E T
N X Q F I U R E E
C B Z A X G L B E
S E Y E N A C J N

# Spies like us!

Use this code wheel to crack the message on the pad.
It will reveal a question.

# Wheel of mystery

Use this code wheel to find out what the message on the pad says.

# Word trail

Use the picture clues to fill in the word trail.
The last letter of each word is the first of the next word.

# Marrow maze

Starting at number 1, connect the dots to complete the maze.
Help Mr Vegpatch find his prize marrow.

1
2
69
68
66
67
4
20
19
12
11
23
24
3
9
10
6   15   16   5
64
65   21   22
57
56
59
58
8   7
13   14
62
51   18   17
50   63   25   26
40   39
35   36   54   28   27
61   55
52   60
29   30
53
32
44
43   31
37   38
45
34   33   47   46
41
42
48
49

# Chicken coop maze

Guide the chick through the coop to its mother.

# Quiz time

How many stomachs does a cow have?

a) 2 ☐
b) 9 ☐
c) 4 ☐
d) 1 ☐

# Puzzle wheel

Write the first letter of each picture in the space in the middle of the puzzle wheel.

You will spell a girl's name.

You will spell the name of a tree.

# Hide-and-seek

Count how many bats, ghosts, and skulls are hidden in this picture.
Write the numbers in the boxes.

bats ghosts skulls

# Monkey problems

Do the problems, then write the answers as words
to complete the crossword.

**a** → 3 × 3 =      **b**  5 + 3  =      **d**  10 − 2 =

**a** ↓ 11 + 8 =      **c**  6 × 3  =      **e**  4 × 4 =

# Quiz time

What is the opening at the top of a volcano called?

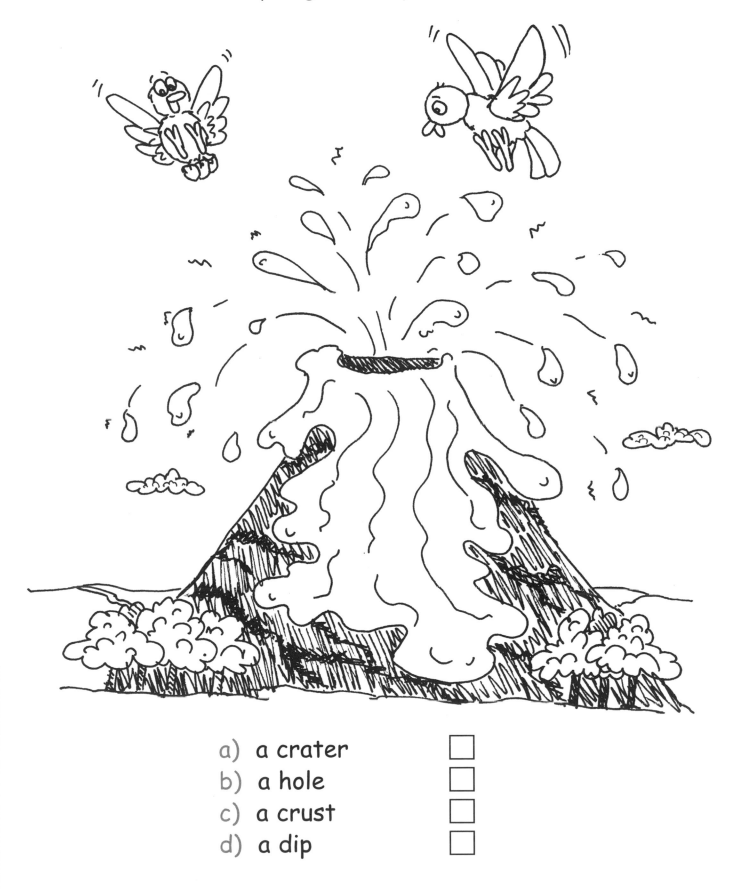

a) a crater ☐
b) a hole ☐
c) a crust ☐
d) a dip ☐

# Ancient messages

Long ago, American Indians sent messages using smoke signals from campfires.

American Indians wrote messages on the ground by scratching lines with a stick, or laying stones in patterns. They also sent messages by beating drums. The sound could be heard miles away.

# Ancient symbols

Here are some of the code symbols American Indians may have used:

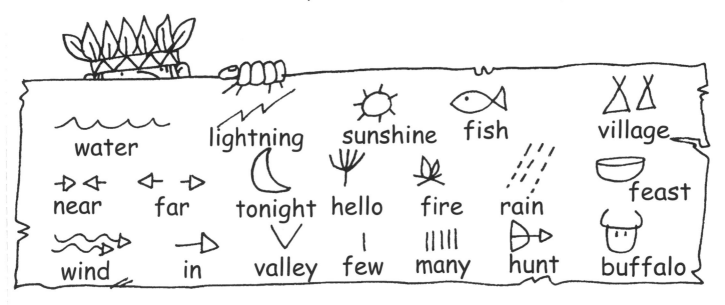

water    lightning    sunshine    fish    village

near    far    tonight    hello    fire    rain    feast

wind    in    valley    few    many    hunt    buffalo

Here are some messages.
What do you think they say? Write the messages on the lines.

Now try to make up some of
your own symbols for the
words below.

cloud    tree    path

day    horse    bird

# Wizard challenge!

How many more of the following pattern can you find in this grid?
Write the number in the box at the bottom of the page.

group

# Who's-who crossword

The numbers in the grid go with the numbers by the witches and wizards. Using the names below, count the squares in the grid to work out who is who.

WILLIAM    WENDY    WINNIE

WALTER    WARDOLPH    WANDA

# When **dinosaurs** ruled

Trace the lines, then use crayons to finish the picture.

# Break in!

Thieves are breaking into the bank's safe.
Guide the police through the maze to the thieves.

# What's the time, Wardolph?

Wardolph has lost his watch. Look at the times in the boxes on the
next page and choose the right time for each of his actions.
Write the correct times in the shaded boxes.

Wardolph waking up

Wardolph eating breakfast

Wardolph leaving his house

Wardolph getting on a magic carpet

| 10:00am | 1:15pm | 8:00am | 6:30pm |
|---------|--------|--------|--------|

| 8:30am | 9:00pm | 10:20am | 12:30pm |
|--------|--------|---------|---------|

Wardolph outside **Wanda's Wands**

Wardolph leaving **Wanda's Wands**

Wardolph at home having a drink

Wardolph asleep with his new wand

# Liftoff!

Complete the grids by filling in the missing numbers.

**1**

| 9 | × |   | = | 18 |
|---|---|---|---|----|
| − | ■ | − | ■ | ÷ |
|   | ÷ | 1 | = |   |
| = | ■ | = | ■ | = |
|   | × |   | = | 6 |

**2**

| 5 | + |   | = | 11 |
|---|---|---|---|----|
| + | ■ | − | ■ | + |
|   | − | 4 | = |   |
| = | ■ | = | ■ | = |
| 12 | + |   | = | 14 |

**3**

| 10 | × |   | = | 20 |
|----|---|---|---|----|
| ÷ | ■ | + | ■ | ÷ |
|   | − | 1 | = |   |
| = | ■ | = | ■ | = |
| 2 | + |   | = | 5 |

**4**

| 2 | + |   | = | 4 |
|---|---|---|---|---|
| + | ■ | − | ■ | + |
|   | − |   | = |   |
| = | ■ | = | ■ | = |
| 11 | + |   | = | 11 |

# Quiz time

How many legs does an octopus have?

a) 2 ☐
b) 4 ☐
c) 5 ☐
d) 8 ☐

# Jumble grumble

Unscramble these anagrams to make new words.
The pictures are clues. Write the words on the lines.

| rebcige | eehhggdo |

_____

_____

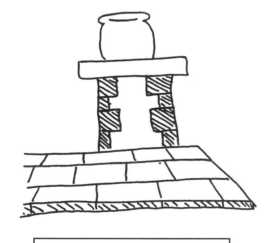

| mihyecn | dastlooto |

_____                    _____

# Quiz time

In which country were fireworks invented?

a) Italy ☐
b) China ☐
c) Australia ☐
d) England ☐

# On the move

Trace the lines, then use crayons to finish the picture.

# Your own secret code

Use the boxes to make up your own secret code.
Now write a message on the pad.

a b c d e f g h i j k l m

n o p q r s t u v w x y z

120

# Secret agent's message

Here is a coded message from a secret agent.
See if you can read it.

# Moggy maze

The little kitten is tangled in a ball of yarn.
Guide the kitten out of the maze.

MILK

# Pirate maze

Starting at number 1, connect the dots to complete the maze.
Help Paddy Pirate find his parrot.

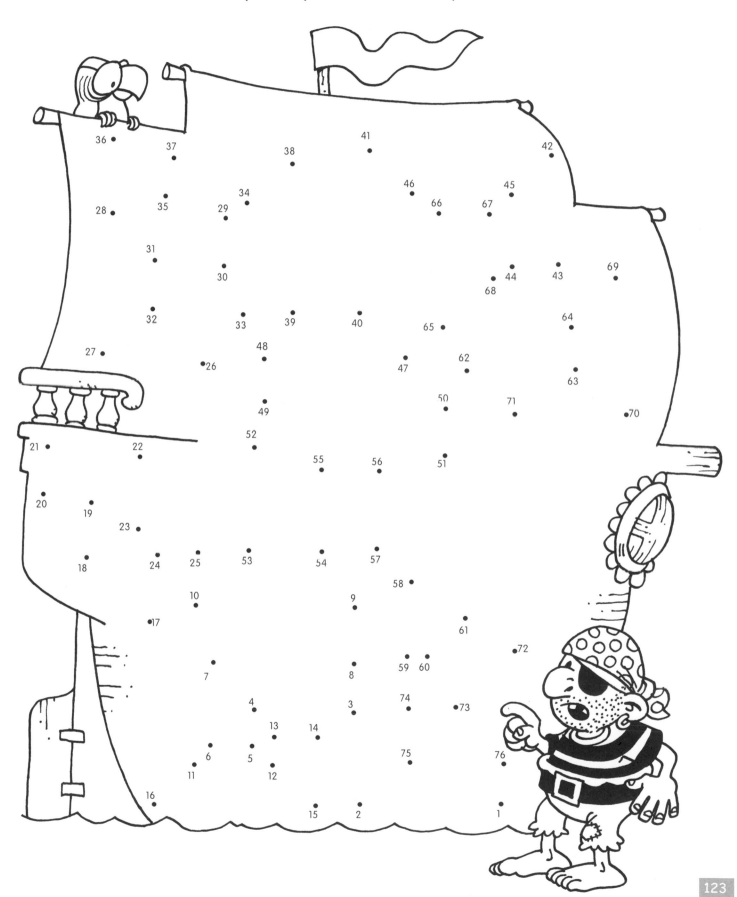

# Ski **numbers**

Look in this grid for the answers to these problems.

6 x 11 =        9 x 9 =        46 − 39 =

23 + 48 =        33 ÷ 3 =        26 − 22 =

20 ÷ 4 =        14 + 16 =

| S | I | X | T | Y | S | I | X | A |
|---|---|---|---|---|---|---|---|---|
| E | B | Z | C | U | D | P | R | E |
| V | Q | S | F | X | V | G | T | A |
| E | L | E | V | E | N | B | H | D |
| N | H | V | C | I | F | H | I | G |
| T | J | E | K | W | I | L | R | O |
| Y | P | N | J | Q | T | M | T | F |
| O | X | Q | F | O | U | R | Y | I |
| N | V | R | L | S | K | U | P | V |
| E | I | G | H | T | Y | O | N | E |

# Spooky wood **word puzzle**

Look in the grid for 11 animals. You will find the words by reading across or down. Circle the words as you find them.

```
B  A  T  R  S  C  V  Y  O
S  R  A  T  Z  M  L  D  P
P  N  F  O  Q  C  R  O  W
I  H  A  W  D  B  X  G  B
D  J  A  L  X  F  F  A  E
E  L  I  Z  A  R  D  I  E
R  H  F  D  Y  O  D  F  S
C  A  T  I  B  G  W  H  Z
S  D  G  R  H  X  O  J  X
B  U  T  T  E  R  F  L  Y
```

# Wandering wizard

Help the wandering wizard find the path to the crystal ball.

# Crossword puzzle

Use the clues to complete this crossword.

1. This person travels in space
2. Use this to wash your hair
3. The hair on a man's chin
4. The opposite of thin
5. The hottest season of the year
6. You wash with this

# Frogman's flipper

The frogman's diving at half the speed. He's lost his flipper among the reeds! Can you see it?

# Fishy tale

Follow the lines to connect the fishermen to their catch.
Which fisherman has caught the biggest fish?

# Puzzle wheel

Write the first letter of each picture in the spaces in the middle of each puzzle wheel.

You will spell the name of a fish.

You will spell the name of a country.

# Quiz time

How does a squid defend itself?

a) by making a loud noise ☐
b) by squirting ink ☐
c) by hiding in seaweed ☐
d) by turning red ☐

# Fast **forward**

Design a city of the future. What changes would there be?

# A-maze in words!

Find your way through the maze to the bookshelf by following the describing words (adjectives).

smelly

sad

naughty

swim

dance

move

fly

merry

sulky

shaky

sit

stand

pretty

lovely

drive

tall

bendy

walk

run

happy

jump

hop

skip

# Word **trail**

Use the picture clues to fill in the word trail.
The last letter of each word is the first of the next word.

# Where in the **world**?

There are the names of eight countries hidden in this grid.
Circle the words as you find them.

| M | E | X | I | C | O | X | S | J |
|---|---|---|---|---|---|---|---|---|
| A | D | F | L | M | B | I | O | A |
| L | Z | I | T | A | L | Y | X | P |
| A | G | Y | V | G | H | A | N | A |
| Y | J | F | P | K | A | I | W | N |
| S | H | T | C | R | Z | Q | I | Q |
| I | R | E | L | A | N | D | U | P |
| A | R | D | K | M | X | H | G | E |
| J | K | C | T | U | P | U | I | R |
| T | U | R | K | E | Y | E | M | U |

# Batty problems

Do the problems, then write the answers as words
to complete the crossword.

a   50 ÷ 5 =
b   99 ÷ 9 =
c   3 × 3 =

d   45 + 7 =
e↓  4 + 12 =
e→  28 ÷ 4 =

f   150 ÷ 50 =
g   6 × 2 =
h   1 × 1 =

# Eye-spy

Count the pairs of eyes that you can see in this picture, and that can see you! Write the number on the cauldron.

# Haunted house

Trace the lines, then use crayons to finish the picture.

# The **Muffet** mystery

She's happily eating her curds and whey, but something's hiding to ruin her day! Can you find it?

# It's a jumble

Unscramble these anagrams to make new words.
The pictures are clues. Write the words on the lines.

epolteneh

kornigc arihc

_____

_____

danlec

lisrequr

_____

_____

# Mouse maze

Starting at number 1, connect the dots to complete the maze.
Help Milly Mouse find the cheese.

# Crazy maze

Shade areas marked with a dot. Start at the arrow and find the way out of the maze.

# Literary numbers

Do the problems, then write the answers as words
to complete the crossword.

**a**   14 + 3 =     **c**   5 × 8  =     **f**  16 + 4  =

**b↓**  15 ÷ 3 =     **d**  20 ÷ 10 =     **g**  30 ÷ 15 =

**b→**  68 ÷ 17 =     **e**  90 ÷ 30 =     **h**  10 × 2  =

146

# Abracadabra!

Starting with number 1, connect the dots to find out what the wizard has accidentally conjured up!

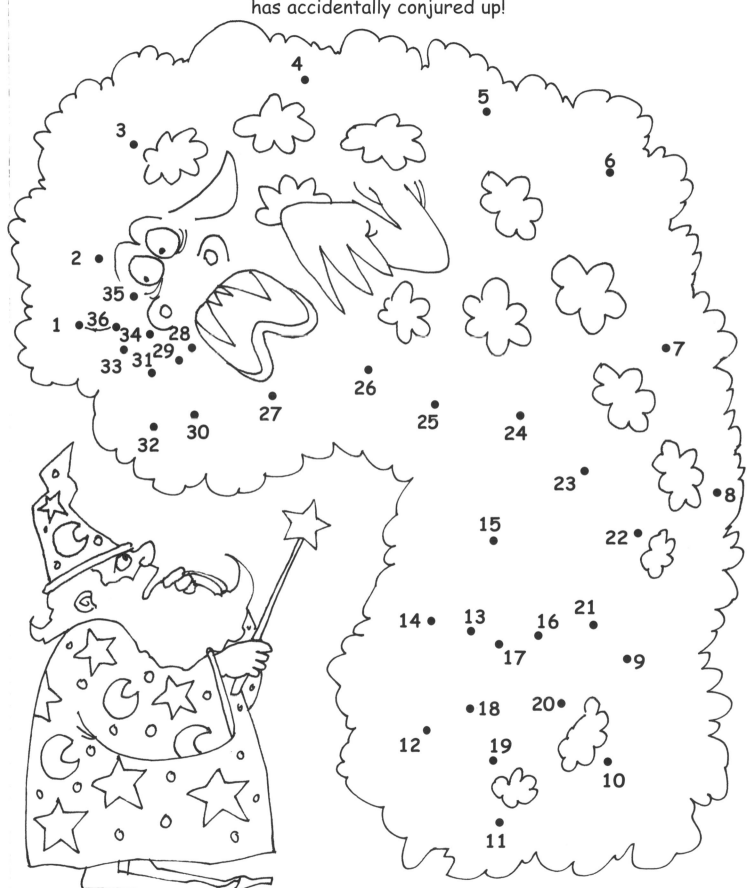

# Code crazy!

Look at the code on this page. Use it to work out the messages on the next three pages.

| a | b | c | d | e | f |
|---|---|---|---|---|---|
| | | | | | |

| g | h | i | j | k | l |
|---|---|---|---|---|---|
| | | | | | |

| m | n | o | p | q | r |
|---|---|---|---|---|---|
| | | | | | |

| s | t | u | v | w | x |
|---|---|---|---|---|---|
| | | | | | |

| y | z |
|---|---|
| | |

# Secret invitation

The picture is a clue to the message on the invitation.
Can you crack the code?

# Woodland wonder!

This secret message has been pinned to a tree.
Can you work it out?

# Where be the treasure?

Use the code to find out where the pirates have hidden the treasure.

# Cake bake

This chef has just baked the most amazing cake you have ever seen.
What does it look like? What delicious things has
he decorated it with?

# Lamp overboard

Poor Aladdin has lost his lamp. Can you help him?

# A **jolly holly** maze

Ho, ho, ho your way through this festive maze.

# Quiz time

Which part of its body does a snake use to listen with?

a) tongue ☐
b) eyes ☐
c) tail ☐
d) teeth ☐

# Number crunchers

Complete the grids by filling in the missing numbers.

**1**

|   |   |   |   |   |
|---|---|---|---|---|
|   | + | 7 | = | 8 |
| + | ■ | − | ■ | + |
| 9 | − |   | = |   |
| = | ■ | = | ■ | = |
|   | + | 5 | = | 15 |

**2**

|   |   |   |   |   |
|---|---|---|---|---|
| 8 | − | 4 | = |   |
| + | ■ | + | ■ | + |
|   | − | 2 | = | 3 |
| = | ■ | = | ■ | = |
| 13 | − |   | = | 7 |

**3**

|   |   |   |   |   |
|---|---|---|---|---|
| 13 | − |   | = | 3 |
| + | ■ | − | ■ | + |
|   | + | 2 | = |   |
| = | ■ | = | ■ | = |
| 20 | − |   | = | 12 |

**4**

|   |   |   |   |   |
|---|---|---|---|---|
|   | + | 2 | = | 12 |
| − | ■ | − | ■ | − |
| 3 | + |   | = |   |
| = | ■ | = | ■ | = |
| 7 | + | 1 | = |   |

# Which hat?

Follow the strings to see who has which hat.

1          2          3          4

# Dragon differences

There are eight differences between these two pictures.
Can you spot them?

# Jigsaw puzzle

Can you see the jigsaw pieces that go together?
Draw lines to connect the pairs.

# What's gone wrong?

The artist has drawn some silly things in this picture.
Can you find them?

# On safari

Trace the lines, then use the crayons to finish the picture.

# Puzzle wheel

Write the first letter of each picture in the spaces
in the middle of each puzzle wheel.

You will spell the
name of a fruit.

You will spell the
name of a fruit.

# Quiz time

How many teeth does the average adult have?

a)  22  ☐
b)  32  ☐
c)  42  ☐
d)  52  ☐

# Market maze

Starting at number 1, connect the dots to complete the maze.
Help Mrs Fusslebussle find her umbrella.

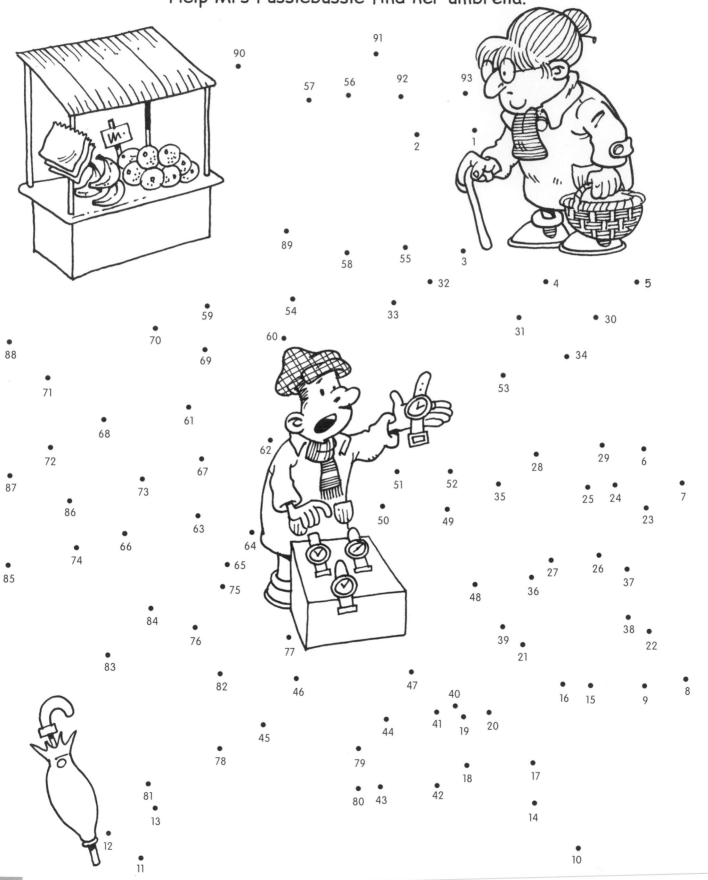

# Mighty maze

Make your way through the maze.

# A **giant** step

Both these pictures may look the same, but there are eight differences, so look again! Circle the differences as you find them.

# Questions and answers

The answers to these questions can be found in the boxes.
Draw lines to match the questions to the answers.

1. What is the opposite of heavy?

2. What appears during the sun and rain?

| horse |
| --- |
| rice |
| light |
| space shuttle |
| rainbow |

3. What does a jockey ride?

4. What grows in a paddy field?

5. What do astronauts travel in?

# Hidden word

Cross out the letters that appear twice in the grid.
The letters that are left spell the name of a tree.
Write your answer on the line below.

| D | U | N | F | Q |
|---|---|---|---|---|
| B | O | C | I | M |
| R | C | D | L | A |
| U | Q | I | M | R |
| N | F | K | L | B |

# Word trail

Use the picture clues to fill in the word trail.
The last letter of each word is the first of the next word.

# Quiz time

What are penguins covered in?

a) feathers ☐
b) fur ☐
c) scales ☐
d) rubber ☐

# Clever crossword

Do the problems, then write the answers as words to complete the crossword.

19 − 16 =

29 − 12 =

8 + 4 =

4 x 5 =

25 ÷ 5 =

30 − 15 =

# Party time

The witches and wizards are having a great time at the party.
Use crayons to finish the picture.

# Jumble scramble

Unscramble these anagrams to make new words.
The pictures are clues. Write the words on the lines.

trewa ylli

_____

rrottca

_____

asdewee

_____

nooxashep

_____

# Quiz time

In which country would you find pyramids and sphinxes?

a) Australia ☐
b) Egypt ☐
c) India ☐
d) France ☐

# Pot of gold!

# Connect the dots to complete the maze.
## Guide the man to the pot of gold.

179

# Afternoon tea

The jungle is patiently waiting to see who has been invited to afternoon tea! Can you find Marmaduke Monkey?

# Quiz time

Which bird lays the largest eggs?

a) an emu ☐
b) an ostrich ☐
c) a golden eagle ☐
d) a turkey ☐

# Sea scene

Trace the lines, then use crayons to finish the picture.

# Desert puzzle

Look in this grid for the answers to these problems.

6 x 7 =          34 + 65 =          14 + 25 =
56 ÷ 8 =         25 x 2 =           94 − 85 =
23 − 9 =         60 ÷ 3 =

| T | F | O | U | R | T | E | E | N |
| H | O | Q | W | E | T | Y | U | I |
| I | R | I | O | P | A | S | D | N |
| R | T | W | E | N | T | Y | X | E |
| T | Y | F | G | H | J | K | L | T |
| Y | T | Z | N | F | I | F | T | Y |
| N | W | C | I | V | B | M | Q | N |
| I | O | W | N | E | R | T | Y | I |
| N | U | I | E | S | E | V | E | N |
| E | A | D | G | J | D | S | B | E |

# Quiz time

On average, which animal has the longest life span?

a) an elephant ☐
b) a giant tortoise ☐
c) a donkey ☐
d) a crocodile ☐

# Copy the picture

Use the grid to help you draw the picture, copying square by square.

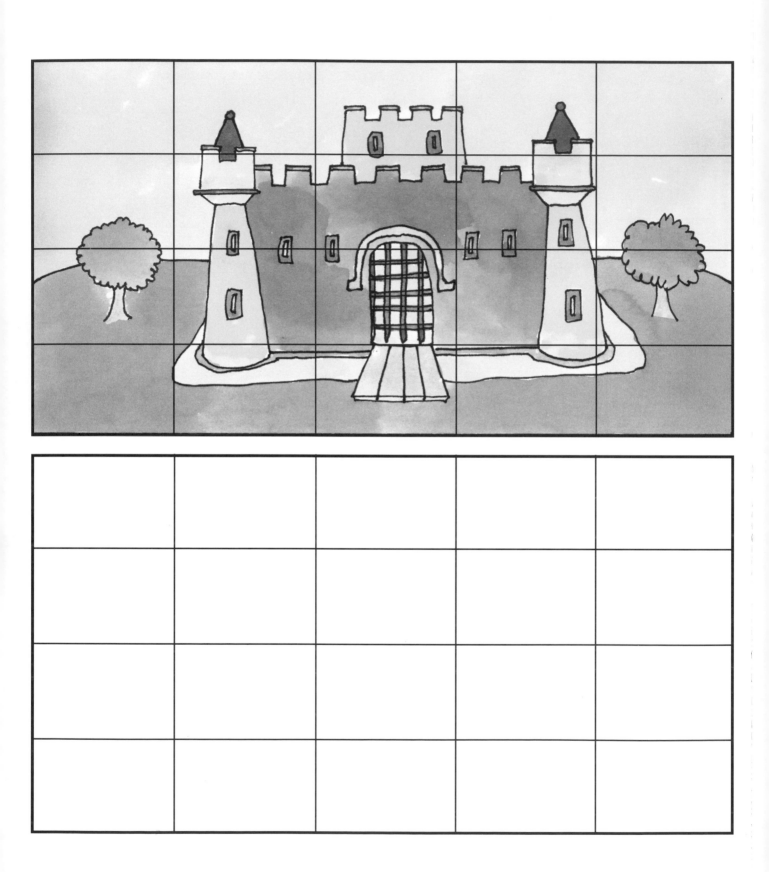

# Potions

The wizard is very careful about weighing the ingredients for his magic potions. This is what he needs to make his invisible spell:

| | | |
|---|---|---|
| 10g of frogspawn | 25g of crows' feet | 2kg of tentacles |
| 50g of sharks' teeth | 100g of dragon scales | 1kg of green slime |

Work out the following:

The heaviest item is ...............................................................

The lightest item is ...............................................................

Key:
1000g = 1kg

# Quiz time

Which insects communicate with one another by dancing?

a) butterflies ☐
b) spiders ☐
c) bees ☐
d) beetles ☐

# Bug catcher

This girl is trying to catch the biggest and strangest bug she's ever seen!
What do you think it looks like?

# Muddy maze

Reach the gate at the end of the maze before the bull gets you!

# Morning maze

Starting at number 1, connect the dots to complete the maze.
Help Hetty find her homework.

# Alien adversity

This alien's spaceship is hard to find.
Could you help him, if you don't mind?

# Quiz time

How often are the Olympic Games held?

a) every year ☐
b) every 2 years ☐
c) every 4 years ☐
d) every 6 years ☐

# Puzzle cobweb

Write the first letter of each picture in the space at the middle of the cobweb. Unscramble the letters to spell the name of something witches brew their potions in.

# Mole hill madness

Complete the grids by filling in the missing numbers.

**1**

| 2 | + |  | = | 12 |
|---|---|---|---|---|
| + | ■ | − | ■ | + |
|  | − | 3 | = |  |
| = | ■ | = | ■ | = |
| 9 | + |  | = | 16 |

**2**

| 12 | + |  | = | 14 |
|---|---|---|---|---|
| − | ■ | + | ■ | − |
|  | − | 2 | = |  |
| = | ■ | = | ■ | = |
| 4 | + |  | = | 8 |

**3**

| 4 | + |  | = | 12 |
|---|---|---|---|---|
| + | ■ | − | ■ | + |
|  | − | 2 | = |  |
| = | ■ | = | ■ | = |
| 14 | + |  | = | 20 |

**4**

| 10 | + |  | = | 16 |
|---|---|---|---|---|
| − | ■ | + | ■ | − |
|  | − | 4 | = |  |
| = | ■ | = | ■ | = |
| 5 | + |  | = | 15 |

# Midnight miaowing!

The cat's noise is keeping everyone awake. Draw the angry residents in the windows.

# Crossword puzzle

Complete this crossword grid. The pictures are clues to the words.

1. This helps you to work out problems
2. A long, thin orange vegetable
3. Keeps you dry in the rain
4. You go to sleep in one of these
5. An Inuit lives in this
6. This plant has red berries and green pointed leaves

# Quiz time

Which is the largest creature ever to have lived on Earth?

a) tyrannosaurus rex ☐
b) blue whale ☐
c) elephant ☐
d) walrus ☐

# Medieval madness

Trace the lines, then use the crayons to finish the picture.

# What's gone wrong?

The artist has drawn some silly things in this picture.
Can you find them?

# A **fairy** flit

Both these pictures may look the same, but there are eight differences, so look again! Circle them as you find them.

# A maze in a haze

It's too foggy for a frog! This little frog has got lost in the fog on the way home to his supper. Can you guide him through the maze?

# Book maze

Starting at number 1, connect the dots to complete the maze.
Help Baz Bookworm find his way to his bookmark.

# Quiz time

What type of dance involves moving
under a low horizontal pole?

a) a waltz ☐
b) a limbo ☐
c) the twist ☐
d) the pogo ☐

# Questions and answers

The answers to these questions can be found in the boxes.
Draw lines to match the questions to the answers.

1. What is the room at the top of a house?

| cook |
| --- |
| stallion |
| tomorrow |
| attic |
| butter |

2. What is the day after today?

3. What do you spread on bread?

4. What is a male horse called?

5. What do chefs do?

# Word wizard

Help the word wizard to unscramble these letters and reveal the missing ingredient for his spell.

# Formula 1 numbers

Do the problems, then write the answers as words
to complete the crossword.

**a** 20 – 11 =          **d** 4 × 2 =          **g** 144 ÷ 12 =
**b** 6 + 5 =            **e** 12 + 4 =          **h** 5 × 2  =
**c** 150 ÷ 15 =         **f** 99 ÷ 9 =          **i** 7 ÷ 7 =

# Super villain

This is the evil super villain Baron Otto Von Potatohead.
He has just invented a device that will help him take
over the world. What does it look like?

# Our hero

Phew! Our secret agent James Blond isn't worried.
He's got a gadget that will foil the evil Baron.
What is the secret weapon that will save the world?

# Word trail

Use the picture clues to fill in the word trail.
The last letter of each word is the first of the next word.

# In the dark

Shade areas marked with a dot.
Start at the BIG arrow and find a way out of the cave.

# Quiz time

Where does a kangaroo carry its young?

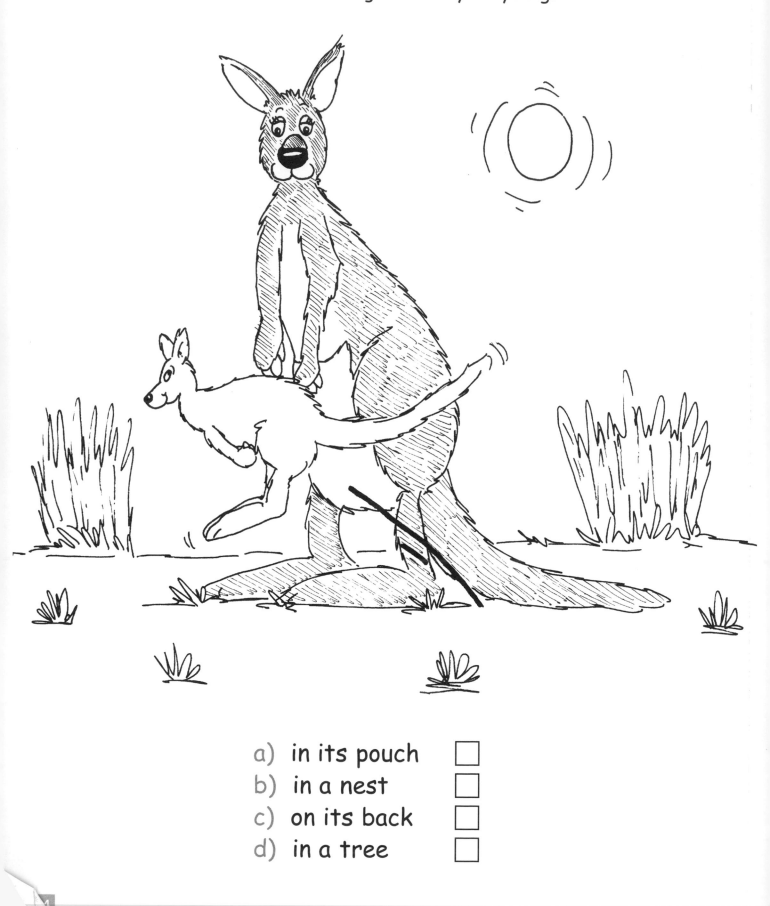

a) in its pouch ☐
b) in a nest ☐
c) on its back ☐
d) in a tree ☐

# Questions and answers

The answers to these questions can be found in the boxes.
Draw lines to match the questions to the answers.

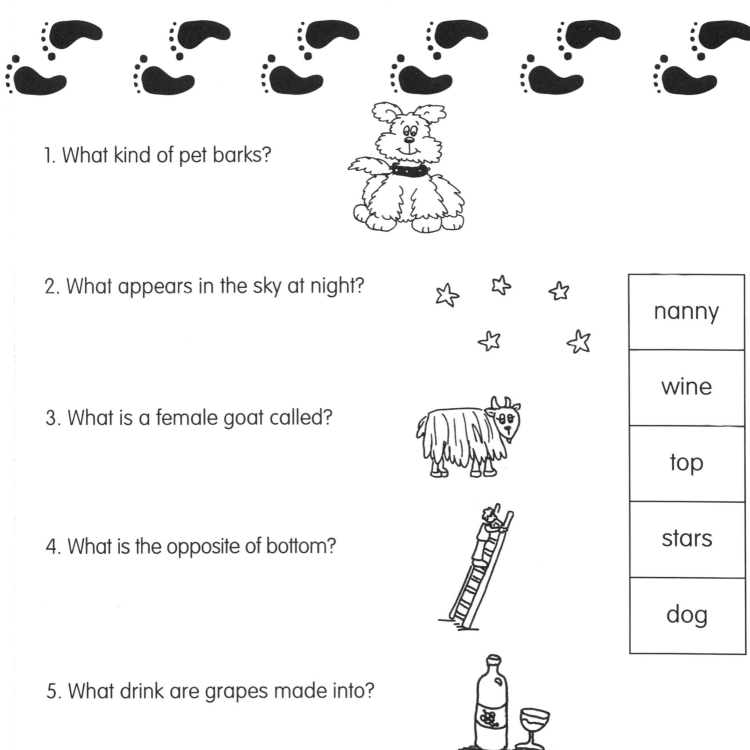

1. What kind of pet barks?

2. What appears in the sky at night?

3. What is a female goat called?

4. What is the opposite of bottom?

5. What drink are grapes made into?

| nanny |
|-------|
| wine |
| top |
| stars |
| dog |

# Rain dance

It's a sweltering day, and George has lost his watering can!
Can you help him find it?

# Number squares

Complete the grids by filling in the missing numbers.

**1**

|   | + | 2 | = | 12 |
|---|---|---|---|----|
| + | ■ | − | ■ | + |
| 7 | − |   | = | 5 |
| = | ■ | = | ■ | = |
| 17 | − | 0 | = |   |

**2**

|   | − | 3 | = | 6 |
|---|---|---|---|---|
| + | ■ | − | ■ | + |
| 2 | + |   | = | 4 |
| = | ■ | = | ■ | = |
| 11 | − | 1 | = |   |

**3**

| 15 | − |   | = | 8 |
|----|---|---|---|---|
| − | ■ | − | ■ | − |
|   | − | 3 | = | 2 |
| = | ■ | = | ■ | = |
| 10 | − | 4 | = |   |

**4**

| 7 | + |   | = | 10 |
|---|---|---|---|----|
| + | ■ | − | ■ | + |
|   | − | 2 | = | 5 |
| = | ■ | = | ■ | = |
| 14 | + | 1 | = |   |

# Up in the air

Trace the lines, then use crayons to finish the picture.

# Coded letter

Wardolph needs help and has sent a letter to Wanda in code. Using the creepy code on page 44, help Wanda to work out the message by writing the letters in the boxes.

Dear Wanda,

!

from
Wardolph

# Quiz time

## Why do wolves howl?

a) to scare other animals ☐
b) to start a fight ☐
c) to announce the full moon ☐
d) to tell other wolves where they are ☐

# Animal magic

Complete the grids by filling in the missing numbers.

**1**

|     | +   | 12  | =   | 24  |
|-----|-----|-----|-----|-----|
| −   | ■   | −   | ■   | −   |
| 6   | +   | 8   | =   |     |
| =   | ■   | =   | ■   | =   |
|     | +   | 4   | =   | 10  |

**2**

| 2   | ×   |     | =   | 6   |
|-----|-----|-----|-----|-----|
| ×   | ■   | ×   | ■   | ×   |
| ■   | ×   | 1   | =   |     |
| =   | ■   | =   | ■   | =   |
| 12  | ×   |     | =   | 36  |

**3**

| 2   | +   | 7   | =   |     |
|-----|-----|-----|-----|-----|
| +   | ■   | −   | ■   | −   |
| 2   | +   |     | =   | 7   |
| =   | ■   | =   | ■   | =   |
|     | −   | 2   | =   | 2   |

**4**

|     | −   | 5   | =   | 5   |
|-----|-----|-----|-----|-----|
| −   | ■   | +   | ■   | −   |
| 2   | +   |     | =   | 5   |
| =   | ■   | =   | ■   | =   |
| 8   | −   | 8   | =   |     |

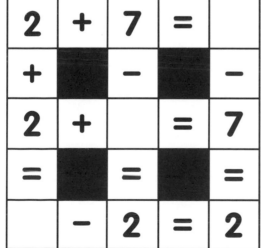

# Wanted!

This is Sheriff Buck Doright. He's putting up wanted posters for Big Bad Bart Brady. What does Bart look like? Draw him on the poster.

# Word puzzle

Find the words in the grid. The pictures are clues.
Circle the words as you find them.

```
H  E  L  N  J  K  S  O  E
F  D  I  M  J  U  N  S  L
G  H  O  S  T  X  S  I  E
E  R  N  E  E  D  L  E  P
F  S  O  N  M  H  I  R  H
Q  J  Y  V  R  S  P  D  A
P  Y  U  B  D  E  P  B  N
L  S  N  A  I  L  E  O  T
U  E  Y  G  V  B  R  M  K
G  T  Y  G  B  U  S  K  L
```

# Robo search

The Robot Racing Championship is about to take place. The 12 finalists have been entered into the computer, but the program has mixed them up. Their names are at the bottom of the page. Can you find them in this grid? You can read them in any direction.

```
X Z T R U H A L L I K I
R S T M A S H S O N B S
E C E S C S O A K I L O
H Y S N A Y S K P C A N
S K R X O L M N N Y Z I
A L K A L L B O N A A C
N O I M M G K O I R R B
G G Y R O B A Y R R M O
A R M A T R O N C Y A O
S R E T S I W T I W G M
G S M A S H A L O T T A
B L A K A N N I B A L K
```

SMASHALOT    CYKLONE
BLAZAR    RAMBOT
GYROBLAST    TWISTER
KILLAHURTZ    KANNIBAL
ARMATRON    KAOS
SONICBOOM    GNASHER

# Starting grid

Can you complete these six Robot Racing words using the words in the box?
When you have done that, fit the words into the grid below.

SM _ _ _

_ _ _ ER

_ _ _ TROL

_ _ _ TERY

MICRO _ _ _ _ _

T _ _ _ SMIT

CHIP   ASH
CON   BAT
RAN   POW

# Crossword puzzle

Complete this crossword grid.
The pictures are clues.

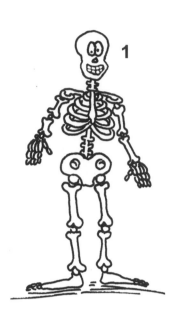

1. A skeleton is made of these
2. These smell lovely!
3. Not brother but . . .
4. Tell the time with this
5. These shine in the sky at night

# Secret postcards

These postcards have been sent from spies in different parts of the world.
Unscramble the words to find out which countries they are from.
The pictures are clues.

MARCIEA

SARSIU

AEKNY

# Pond prince

"That frog prince tale was good for us toads. I never had visitors, now I get loads!"
Can you find the princess?

# Find the **robots**

The names of 12 machines have been entered into the computer, but the program has mixed them up. Their names are printed at the bottom of the page. Can you find them in this grid? You can read them in any direction.

| | | | | | | | | | | | |
|---|---|---|---|---|---|---|---|---|---|---|---|
| B | H | X | I | T | S | A | L | B | B | R | M |
| G | O | B | K | I | C | E | A | H | K | O | A |
| F | V | I | S | T | M | P | A | A | L | B | G |
| T | E | G | R | R | O | B | O | M | A | O | N |
| O | R | T | E | M | O | S | V | Q | S | M | A |
| B | B | R | R | O | B | O | B | A | L | L | T |
| E | O | A | G | A | C | T | R | M | O | I | R |
| L | T | K | M | A | I | G | N | A | A | G | O |
| B | X | R | E | D | N | U | H | T | G | L | N |
| M | M | R | O | B | O | B | U | G | N | I | S |
| I | N | A | B | C | S | U | B | I | G | T | B |
| W | P | R | S | T | G | U | B | A | G | E | M |

**ROBOBUG**  **MEGABUG**
SONICBOOM  BIGTRAK
**MAGNATRON**  THUNDER
WIMBLEBOT  BLASTIX
**ROBOBALL**  SLAM
HOVERBOT  KAOS

# Quiz time

What does a scorpion have at the end of its tail?

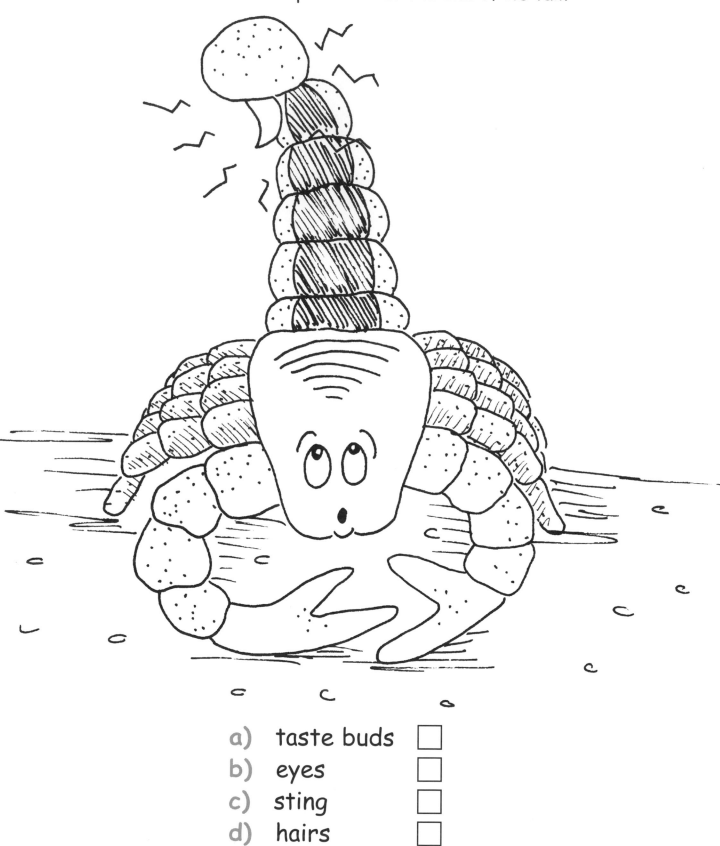

a) taste buds ☐
b) eyes ☐
c) sting ☐
d) hairs ☐

# Kitten numbers

Do the problems, then write the answers as words
to complete the crossword.

→ **a** 35 + 25 =

↓ **a** 35 ÷ 5 =

**b** 30 ÷ 3 =

**c** 18 + 9 =

**d** 9 x 2 =

**e** 5 x 4 =

**f** 200 ÷ 100 =

**g** 50 + 22 =

**h** 21 − 4 =

# Word magic

How many new words can you make from the word **broomstick**?
Write the words in the book.

# broomstick

# Crazy cat shadows

Draw lines to match these crazy cats to their shadows.

# Dressing up

These two pictures may look the same, but there are
10 differences. Can you find them?

# Robot dot-to-dot

Connect the dots to complete these robots.

# Frame it!

Draw a picture of your best friend in this picture frame.

# Quiz time

What does a chameleon change in order to hide itself from predators?

a) its skin tone ☐
b) its tail ☐
c) its fur ☐
d) its home ☐

# Robot maze

Can you find a way through the maze for this racing robot?

# Robot jokes

Why did the robot go crazy?
**It had a screw loose!**

What did the robot have on its gravestone?
**Rust In Peace!**

What do you get if you cross a robot with a vampire?
**Something new-fangled!**

Why do robots go to school?
**For assembly!**

How did the robot get sick?
**It had a bug!**

# Fun in the **snow**

Trace the lines, then use crayons to finish the picture.

# Show-jumping **numbers**

Look in this grid for the answers to these problems.

49 ÷ 7 =          6 + 7 =          9 + 9 =
74 − 62 =         32 ÷ 8 =         16 ÷ 2 =
23 + 27 =         26 + 16 =        5 x 4 =

| F | O | R | T | Y | T | W | O | Q |
|---|---|---|---|---|---|---|---|---|
| O | W | E | W | R | Y | U | T | P |
| U | A | S | E | D | E | G | H | S |
| R | J | X | L | C | I | V | I | E |
| N | Q | E | V | R | G | T | R | V |
| I | O | P | E | A | H | S | T | E |
| F | I | F | T | Y | T | F | E | N |
| K | L | B | C | D | E | R | E | W |
| E | I | G | H | T | E | S | N | J |
| A | N | T | W | E | N | T | Y | K |

# Puzzle wheel

Write the first letter of each picture in the space in the middle
of the puzzle wheel.
You will spell the name of an animal.

# Tidied away

Both these pictures may look the same, but there are eight differences, so look again! Circle the differences as you find them.

# Something fishy

This goldfish needs some fishy friends and a castle to swim around in his bowl. Draw them in to make him really happy.

# Muddled story

This story has been magically muddled.
Help the wizard by numbering the boxes from 1-4 in the correct order.

a little bit of magic. . .

"Feet of toads and tail of dog,
Turn this rabbit into a frog!"

reading the spell

success!

choosing the subject

# Ghastly gallery word puzzle

Look in the grid for the six names at the bottom of the page.
You will find them by reading across or down.

| H | I | D | E | O | U | S | Y | S |
| E | V | I | L | N | M | C | X | A |
| L | N | G | O | I | Y | A | O | D |
| G | H | E | W | G | X | R | G | H |
| A | J | O | S | E | F | Y | A | A |
| V | M | R | T | L | R | D | S | R |
| P | A | G | E | Y | H | D | U | R |
| C | D | E | I | O | R | G | E | Y |
| F | R | A | N | K | I | E | J | X |
| A | Z | V | J | H | P | V | J | T |

Hideous Helga     Mad George     Scary Sue

Frankie Stein     Evil Nigel     Sad Harry

# Machine maze

Can you find a way through the maze for this racing robot?

# Word trail

Use the picture clues to fill in the word trail.
The last letter of each word is the first letter of the next word.

# Witchy **wanderings**

The witch flies away with a worried frown
as her magical wand falls further down. Can you find it?

# Clown dot-to-dot

Starting at number 1, connect the dots to complete the picture.

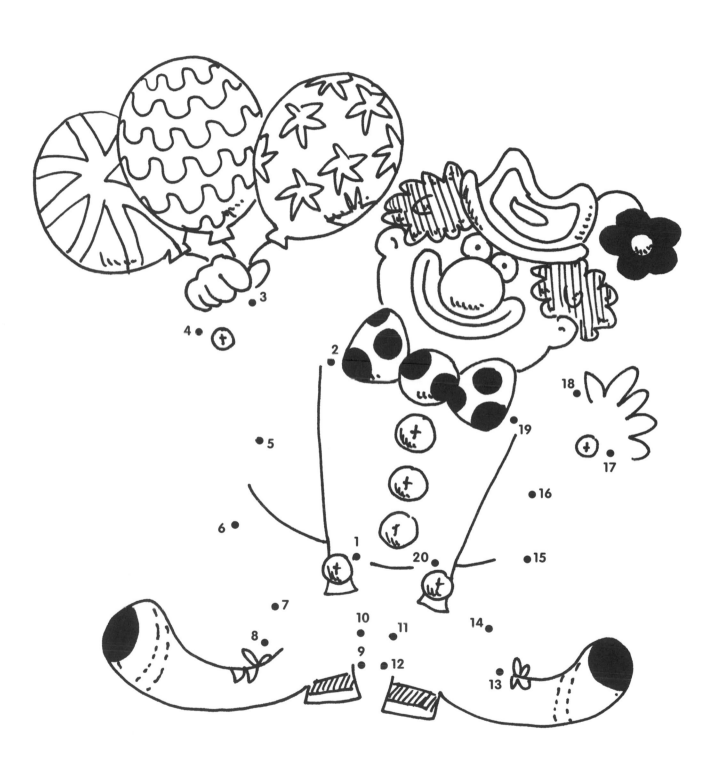

# Gardening

Which of these things can be used when doing the gardening?
Put ticks in the boxes.

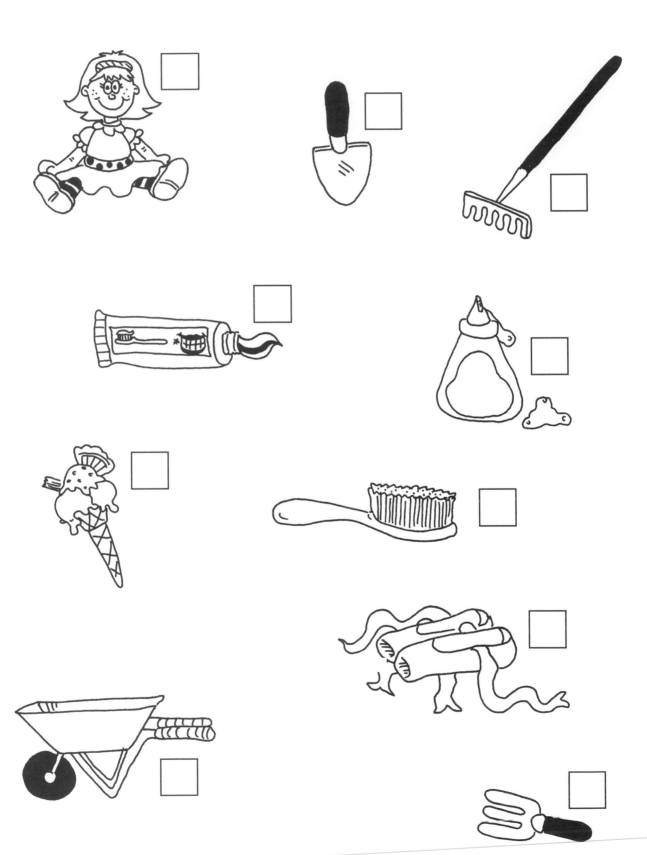

# What's gone **wrong**?

The artist has drawn some silly things in this picture.
Can you find them?

# Sailing numbers

Do the problems, then write the answers as words
to complete the crossword.

**a**   $10 \div 2 =$      **d**   $5 + 3 =$      **g**   $80 \div 8 =$

**b**   $17 + 43 =$      **e**   $10 \times 5 =$      **h**   $7 \div 7 =$

**c**   $25 - 6 =$      **f**   $30 \div 10 =$      **i**   $12 + 7 =$

# Dinosaur sports day

Both these pictures may look the same, but there are eight differences, so look again! Circle the differences as you find them.

# Jumble

Unscramble these anagrams to make new words.
The pictures are clues. Write the words on the lines.

sepilspr

_____

fsur aobdr

_____

teflyubtr

_____

aarml ccokl

_____

# Robot jokes

What's a robot's fave food?
**Micro chips!**

Why was the robot arrested?
**It had robbed the memory bank!**

What sort of music do robots listen to?
**Techno!**

How does a robot shave?
**With a laser blade!**

What do you call a robot that always takes the longest route?
**R2 Detour!**

# Flying tonight!

It is a spooky night for Wanda and her pets to be flying home.
Help them through the starry sky to their cottage.

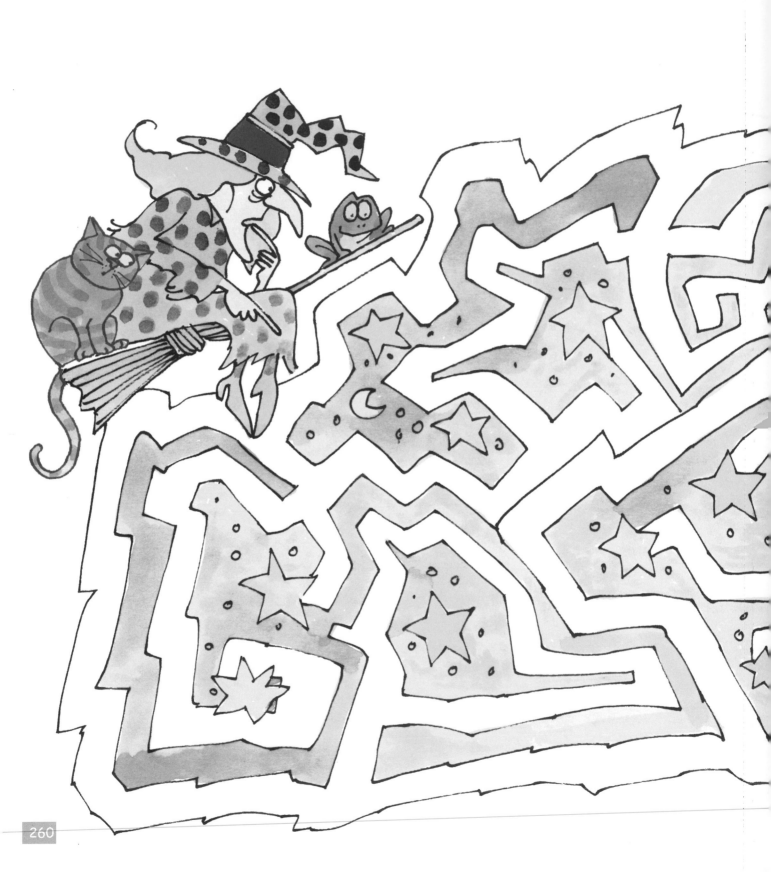

# Woodland **wanderings**

Slowly the creatures come creeping again, but one little mouse
is scared of more rain! Can you find him?

# Dragon drawing

Alfred the wizard has conjured up a magical dragon.
What sort of dragon is it? Does it breathe fire?

# Puzzle wheel

Write the first letter of each picture in the space in the middle of the puzzle wheel. You will spell the name of a planet.

# Hidden word

Cross out the letters that appear twice in the grid.
The letters that are left spell the name of a sea creature.
Write your answer on the line below.

| J | E | D | T | O |
|---|---|---|---|---|
| K | L | G | R | P |
| U | R | H | J | G |
| I | M | A | U | K |
| T | E | A | M | N |

# Puzzle cobweb

Write the first letter of each picture in the space at the middle of the cobweb. Unscramble the letters to make a magical word.

# Magic numbers

Do the problems, then write the answers as words to complete the crossword.

a 21 – 13 =

b 45 ÷ 9 =

c 13 + 7 =

d 150 ÷ 50 =

e → 30 – 11 =

e ↓ 36 ÷ 4 =

f 43 + 27 =

g 22 – 11 =

h 100 ÷ 10 =

i 5 – 4 =

267

# Word machine

How many new words can you make from the words **METAL MADNESS**?
Write them in the box below.

# Daydreamers

Draw what these girls are dreaming about.

# Word trail

Use the picture clues to fill in the word trail.
The last letter of each word is the first of the next word.

# Plant spotting

There are the names of eight flowers and plants hidden in this grid. Circle the words as you find them.

| J | R | E | I | T | U | L | I | P |
| R | O | S | E | L | K | B | Y | A |
| I | O | D | N | P | L | W | C | R |
| K | X | H | Q | A | R | G | A | S |
| C | R | E | F | N | P | Z | C | L |
| H | D | A | I | S | Y | H | T | E |
| D | U | T | M | Y | L | W | U | Y |
| R | K | H | B | U | T | U | S | Q |
| O | T | E | S | K | Q | Z | Y | D |
| M | A | R | I | G | O | L | D | G |

# Junk box

There are junkyard things hidden in this grid. Can you find them?
You can read them in the grid in any direction.
The words are printed on the right.

| T | L | O | B | E | C | R | R | A | C |
| C | H | A | I | N | I | R | G | N | E |
| R | X | Y | V | G | G | B | L | M | B |
| A | P | W | S | I | T | M | O | N | P |
| N | R | H | T | N | N | U | O | A | R |
| E | X | E | R | E | L | O | N | P | T |
| S | T | E | X | V | B | P | A | R | S |
| O | A | L | R | I | L | R | U | Y | T |
| X | P | V | K | T | Q | C | M | G | V |
| S | T | E | E | K | K | S | N | V | X |

CHAIN
CRANE
ENGINE
CAR
TRUCK
BOAT
BIKE
WHEEL
BOLT
NUT

# Questions and answers

The answers to these questions can be found in the boxes.
Draw lines to match the questions to the answers.

1. What does a red traffic light mean?

2. What does a shepherd look after?

| breakfast |
| --- |
| purr |
| snail |
| stop |
| sheep |

3. What is the first meal of the day?

4. What noise do cats make?

5. Which creature carries its home on its back?

275

# Creepy castle dot-to-dot

Starting with number 1, connect the dots to complete the picture.

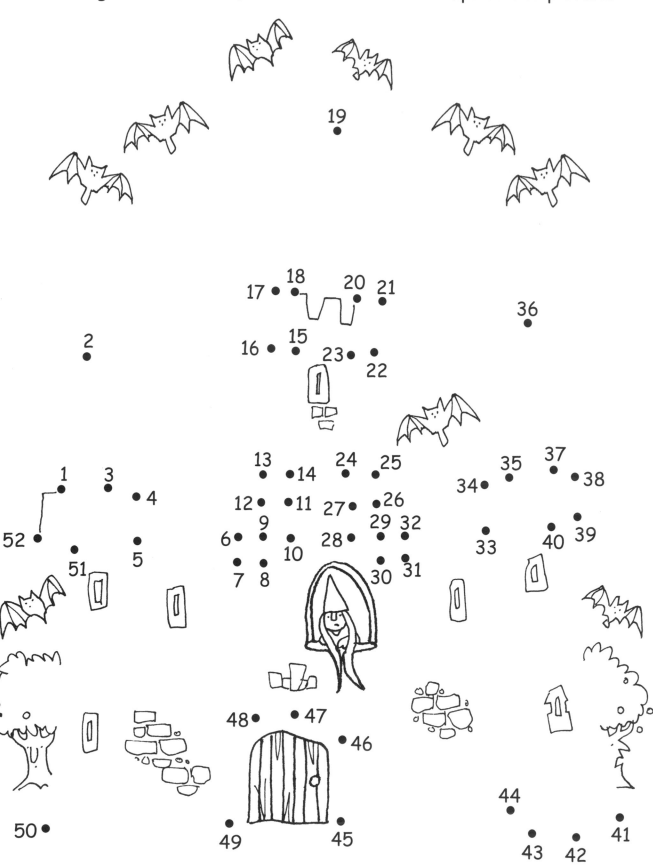

# Number fun

Complete the grids by filling in the missing numbers.

1. 
| 14 | − |   | = | 8 |
| − |   | + |   | − |
|   | + | 4 | = |   |
| = |   | = |   | = |
| 12 | − |   | = | 2 |

2. 
| 18 | − |   | = | 16 |
| − |   | + |   | − |
| 4 | + | 2 | = |   |
| = |   | = |   | = |
|   | − |   | = | 10 |

3. 
| 16 | − |   | = | 13 |
| − |   | + |   | + |
|   | − | 7 | = |   |
| = |   | = |   | = |
| 6 | + |   | = | 16 |

4. 
| 3 | + |   | = | 10 |
| + |   | − |   | + |
| 8 | − |   | = |   |
| = |   | = |   | = |
|   | + | 4 | = | 15 |

277

# Goldilocks

Baby bear laughed about the beds and the food, but his parents were thinking that she had been quite rude! Can you find Goldilocks?

# Quiz time

What do some animals do between winter and spring?

a) go skiing ☐
b) put their warm coats on ☐
c) hibernate ☐
d) play golf ☐

# Words within words

Make new words out of the ones you see here.
How many can you find? Write them on the lines.

CAULIFLOWER

SWEETCORN

GRAPEFRUIT

WATERMELON

PINEAPPLE

# Charging station

These four robots are having their batteries charged.
Can you work out which power points the robots are plugged into?

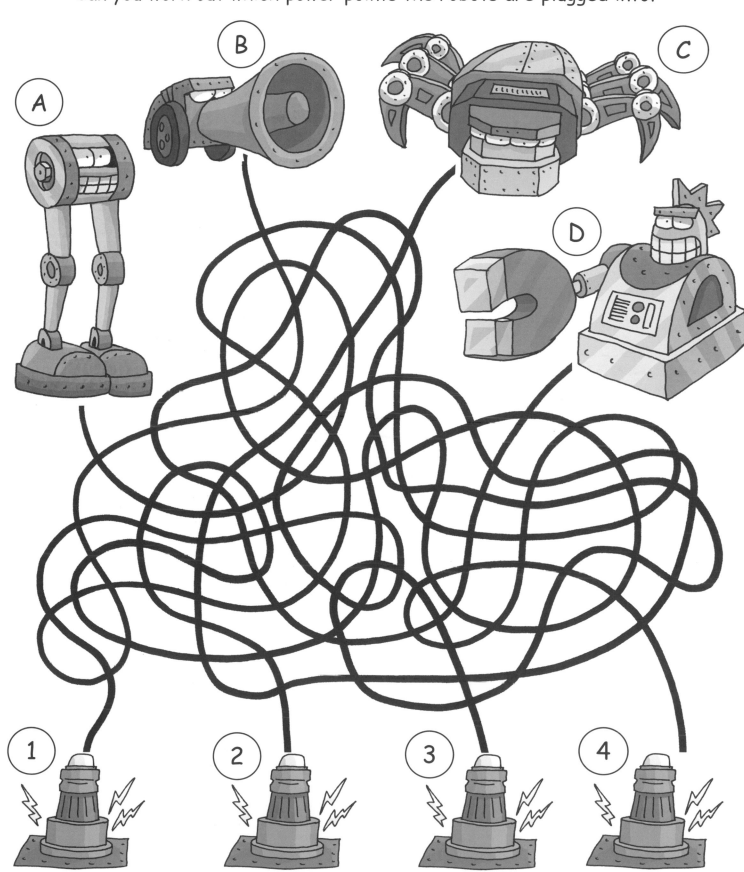

# Jumble

Unscramble these anagrams to make new words.
The pictures are clues. Write the words on the lines.

| rief ecalp | nacdocori |
|---|---|

_____

_____

| eganmobor | ogtsh |
|---|---|

_____

_____

# Quiz time

What is somebody who studies the weather called?

a) a psychologist ☐
b) an architect ☐
c) a linguist ☐
d) a meteorologist ☐

# Tree puzzles

Complete the grids by filling in the missing numbers.

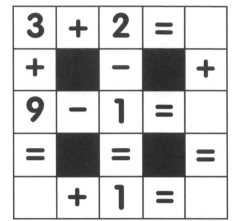

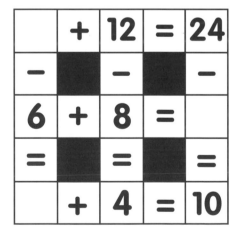

# Spooky numbers

Count the number of things on each line and answer the problems.
Write the answers in the potion bottles.

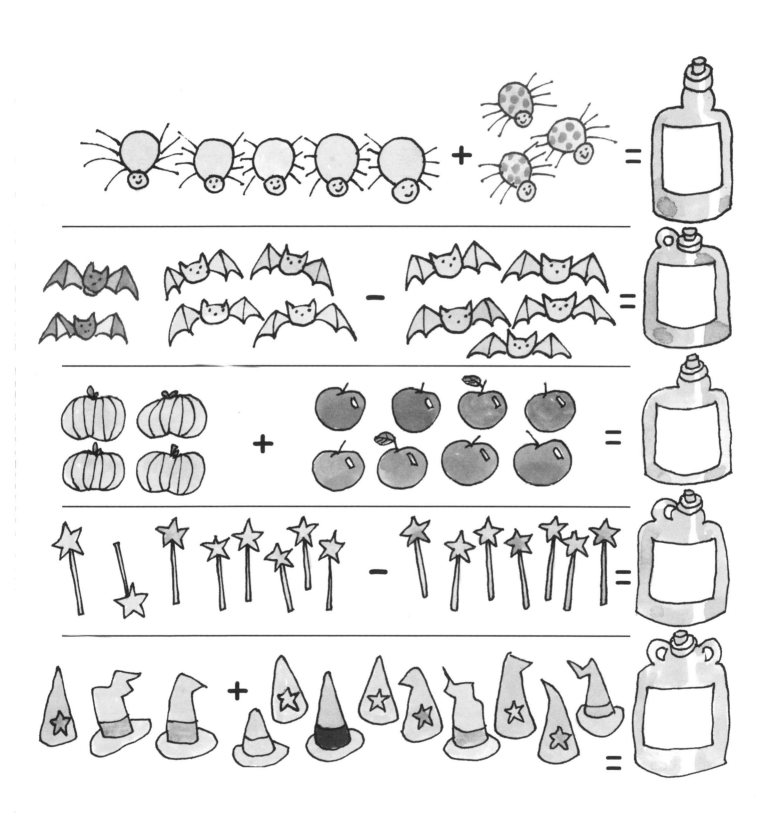

# Cool code

Get your pencils ready!
Use the number code to complete this scene.

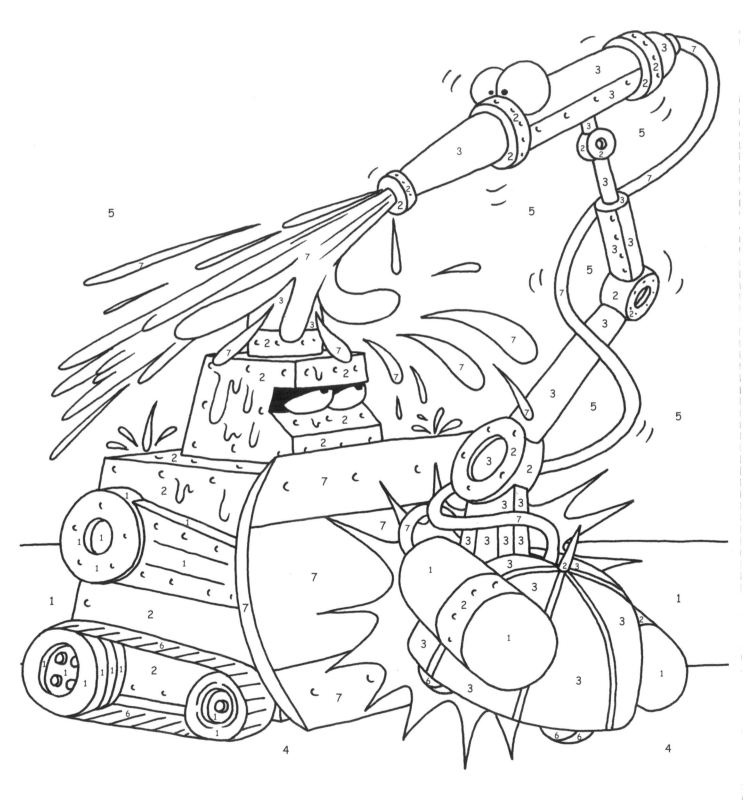

1 = RED          3 = DARK BLUE    5 = ORANGE       7 = LIGHT BLUE
2 = YELLOW       4 = BROWN        6 = BLACK

# Word **puzzles**

What word does this riddle spell out?

My first is in boat
But isn't in coat,
My second is in meat
But isn't in meet,
My third is in talk
But isn't in walk,
My fourth is in travel
But isn't in gravel,
My fifth is in fine
But isn't in find,
My sixth is in rang
But isn't in bang,
My seventh is in yell
But isn't in bell.

## What am I?

The answers to each of the clues below can be formed using the letters in the word **JUNKYARD**.

1. It gets like this at night. (4 letters)

_____

2. Pull hard on a rope. (4 letters)

_____

3. Follows night. (3 letters)

_____

4. Keep peanut butter in. (3 letters)

_____

5. ___ of sunshine. (3 letters)

_____

# Quiz time

In which country is the kimono the national dress for women?

a) Japan ☐
b) China ☐
c) Spain ☐
d) Australia ☐

# Cheesy numbers

Complete the grids by filling in the missing numbers.

**1**

| 5 | + |   | = | 12 |
|---|---|---|---|----|
| + | ■ | + | ■ | + |
| 4 | + |   | = |   |
| = | ■ | = | ■ | = |
|   | + | 12 | = |   |

**2**

| 5 | + | 6 | = |   |
|---|---|---|---|---|
| + | ■ | − | ■ | + |
|   | − | 4 | = | 3 |
| = | ■ | = | ■ | = |
|   | + | 2 | = |   |

**3**

|   | + | 8 | = |   |
|---|---|---|---|---|
| + | ■ | − | ■ | + |
| 6 | − |   | = | 2 |
| = | ■ | = | ■ | = |
| 12 | + |   | = | 16 |

**4**

| 8 | + |   | = | 10 |
|---|---|---|---|----|
| + | ■ | − | ■ | + |
| 8 | − | 2 | = |   |
| = | ■ | = | ■ | = |
|   | + | 0 | = |   |

# Crazy code

Get your pencils ready!
Use the number code to complete this ball machine.

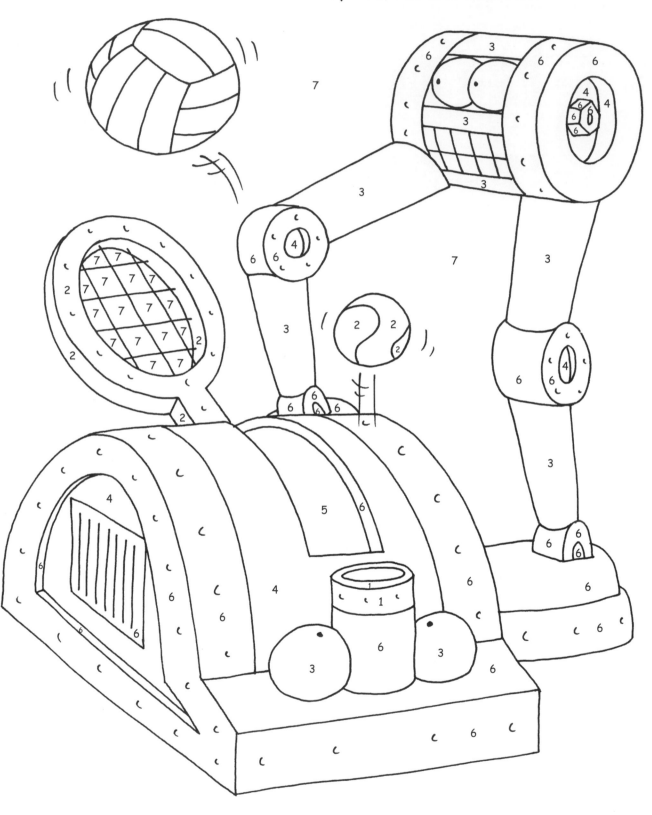

1 = RED          3 = LIGHT GREEN   5 = BLACK       7 = LIGHT BLUE
2 = YELLOW       4 = DARK GREEN    6 = DARK BLUE

# Pet spotting

There are eight pets hidden in this grid.
Circle the words as you find them.

```
R  B  C  A  N  A  R  Y  S
A  W  A  Q  Y  G  J  F  B
B  I  T  A  M  O  U  S  E
B  R  D  C  S  L  K  L  E
I  R  W  V  Z  D  O  G  V
T  H  L  J  S  F  T  O  D
Q  Y  R  B  C  I  D  X  P
U  B  H  A  M  S  T  E  R
H  V  M  T  S  H  S  O  A
P  O  N  Y  E  Y  E  O  M
```

# Animals crossword

The pictures are clues and the numbers show you where each word goes in the grid. Write the words in the crossword.

# Food search

The pictures are clues. Look for these words in the grid.
You will find them by reading across or down.
Circle the words as you find them.

| J | S | E | E | R | Z | U | H | M |
|---|---|---|---|---|---|---|---|---|
| C | K | R | A | M | E | Q | P | O |
| H | C | M | L | H | O | N | E | Y |
| E | G | G | K | E | U | Y | T | E |
| R | S | P | C | W | X | B | H | T |
| R | M | B | H | Q | R | U | L | O |
| I | N | V | E | T | F | R | I | P |
| E | I | J | E | Y | R | G | F | H |
| S | A | U | S | A | G | E | S | U |
| S | D | O | E | H | Y | R | P | Q |

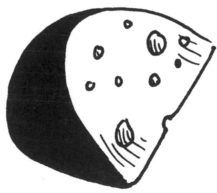

# Happy Humpty

Both these pictures may look the same, but there are eight differences, so look again! Circle the differences as you find them.

# Quiz time

What part of a golden eagle is gold?

a) the beak ☐
b) the neck feathers ☐
c) the feet ☐
d) the tail ☐

# Dino ZOO

Can you match these names to the pictures of the dinosaurs below?
Write them in the spaces beneath the pictures.

## TYRANNOSAURUS REX
## TRICERATOPS
## STEGOSAURUS
## DIPLODOCUS

_____        _____

_____        _____

# Pirate games

It's no good looking, you'll have to shout. The parrot's gone on walkabout! Can you find him?

# Maze bot

Can you guide this robot through the maze?

# Word **puzzles**

Can you fit the words below into the grid? Some of the letters have been added for you.

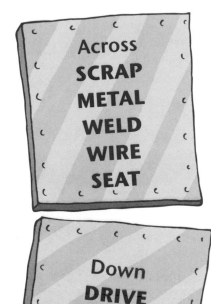

**Across**
**SCRAP**
**METAL**
**WELD**
**WIRE**
**SEAT**

**Down**
**DRIVE**
**TOOL**
**SPANNER**
**SCREW**

The answers to each of the clues can be formed from the letters in the words **ROBOT RACING**.

1. Rodent (3 letters).

2. Water transport (4 letters).

3. Circle (4 letters).

4. The sound a lion makes (4 letters).

5. You are using it now (5 letters).

# Daily blurb

If it wasn't true we'd have to make it up!

### Exclusive!!

Phillipa Fogg has discovered a new species of parrot living in the jungles of Peru. The Daily Blurb has exclusive pictures of the new discovery.

# Quiz time

What is the largest bird in the world?

a) goose ☐
b) vulture ☐
c) ostrich ☐
d) eagle owl ☐

# Disco numbers

Do the problems, then write the answers as words to complete the crossword.

a) 50 – 20 =

a) 3 x 7 =

b) 100 ÷ 4 =

c) 4 x 3 =

d) 20 x 4 =

e) 5 x 3 =

f) 8 x 5 =

g) 21 – 10 =

h) 1000 ÷ 100 =

# Spy's **word puzzle**

The pictures are clues. Look for these words in the grid.
You will find them by reading across or down.
Circle the words as you find them.

| M | J | S | O | R | H | P | I | B |
|---|---|---|---|---|---|---|---|---|
| I | O | C | P | S | I | H | K | I |
| C | A | M | E | R | A | U | L | N |
| R | Z | Q | N | Y | T | Q | B | O |
| O | B | N | C | V | S | E | G | C |
| P | M | S | I | L | P | E | Y | U |
| H | X | T | L | O | Y | R | M | L |
| O | J | Y | W | A | B | U | O | A |
| N | O | T | E | P | A | D | R | R |
| E | K | R | A | M | Q | J | B | S |

# Prehistoric times

Can you crack this letter code to work out the question?
Write the answer on the lines.

## WH ATIS ATYRAN NO SAUR USR EX?

_____

_____

# Workshop maze

Guide the robot to the spanner.

# Broomstick bonanza

Use crayons to finish this picture.

# Quiz time

From which country did the hamburger originate?

a) USA ☐
b) England ☐
c) France ☐
d) Germany ☐

# Alien encounter

Both these pictures may look the same, but there are eight differences, so look again! Circle the differences as you find them.

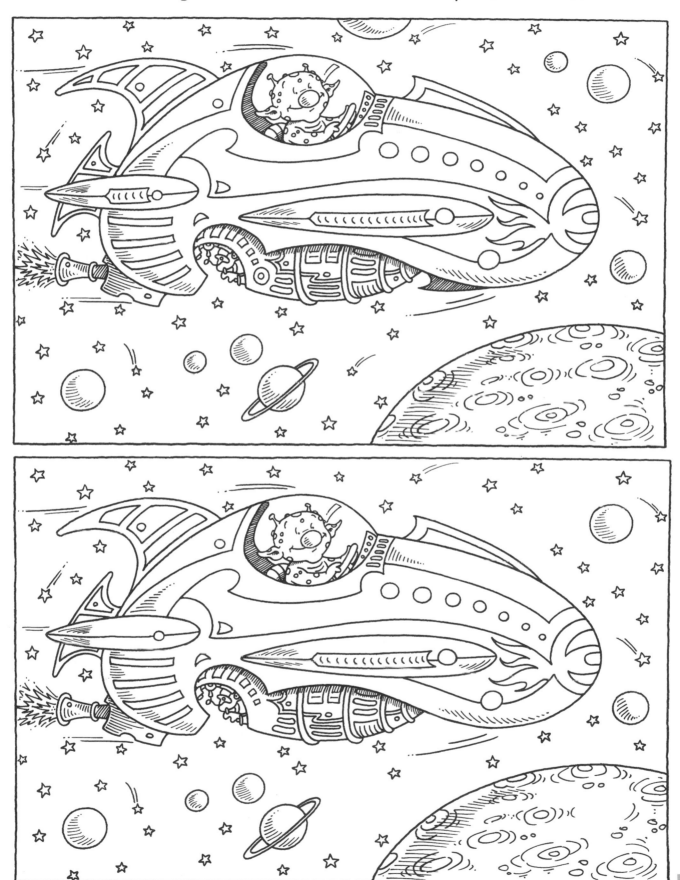

311

# Circuit breaker

Can you work out which of these electronic circuits
is the odd one out?

A

B

C

D

# Word trail

Use the picture clues to fill in the word trail.
The last letter of each word is the first of the next word.

# Junkyard **jumbles**

## Pick a spanner

Look carefully at this pile of spanners. In which order should you pick them up if you want to pick up the top spanner each time?

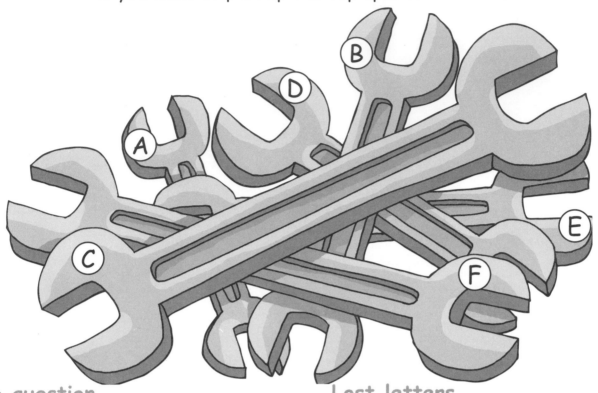

## Cog question

How many cogs can you see here?

## Lost letters

Spot the missing letters of the alphabet and rearrange them to make a robot-related word.

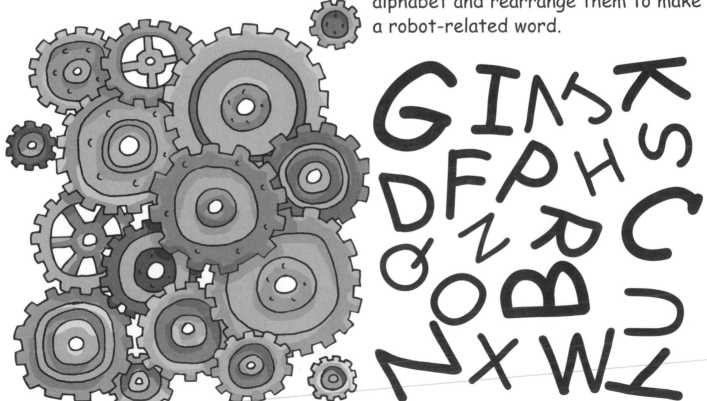

# Gone **fishing**

The fisherman has caught something on the end of his line.
What could it be? Is it a big fish or just an old bicycle?
Draw what you think it is.

# Festive numbers

Look in this word puzzle for the answers to these problems.

16 ÷ 8 =      13 + 12 =      22 - 1 =
20 x 3 =      25 ÷ 5 =      3 x 4 =
19 - 11 =      7 x 6 =

```
T  W  E  N  T  Y  O  N  E
W  A  V  B  W  L  C  M  I
E  N  D  X  O  E  W  P  G
N  F  Q  G  Y  H  Z  I  H
T  J  S  I  X  T  Y  K  T
Y  L  A  M  R  B  N  S  C
F  O  R  T  Y  T  W  O  F
I  O  D  P  F  Q  E  R  I
V  G  T  W  E  L  V  E  V
E  S  H  J  T  I  U  K  E
```

# Quiz **time**

What is the name of the sea between Egypt and Saudi Arabia?

a) Black ☐
b) Pink ☐
c) Green ☐
d) Red ☐

# Whose house?

These witches and wizards have forgotten where they live.
Follow the paths to help them find their way home.

# Spell casting

There are 11 differences between these two pictures.
Can you find them?

# Sounds good!

The pictures are clues for the crossword.
When you have done the crossword, unscramble the letters in the shaded parts to spell a new word.

# Toot toot!

Both these pictures may look the same, but there are eight
differences, so look again!
Circle the differences as you find them.

# Mystery maze

Help the spy through the maze to the magnifying glass.
On the way you will spell the name of a fruit.

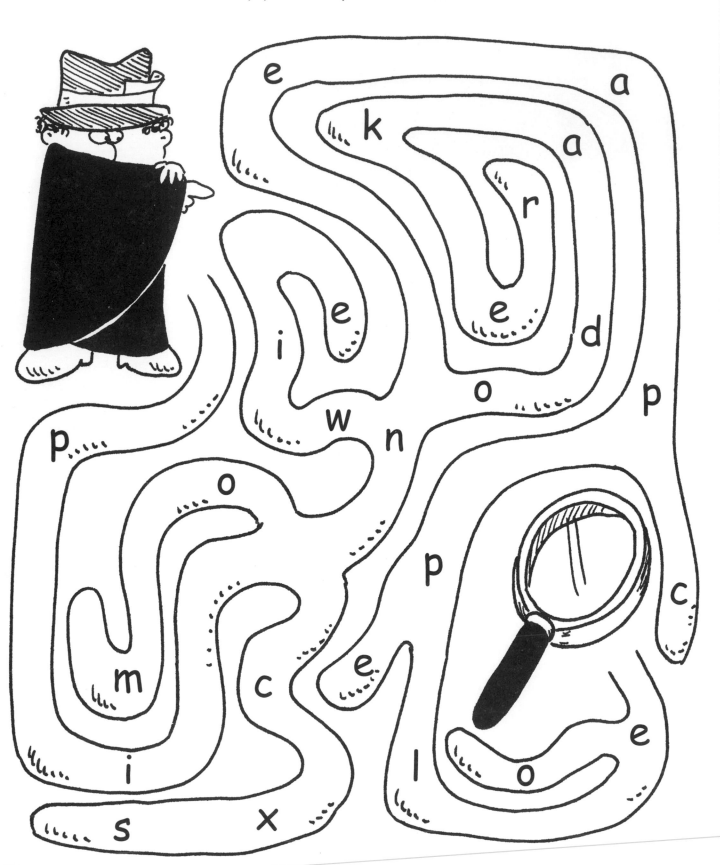

# Quiz time

What is the hyena well known for?

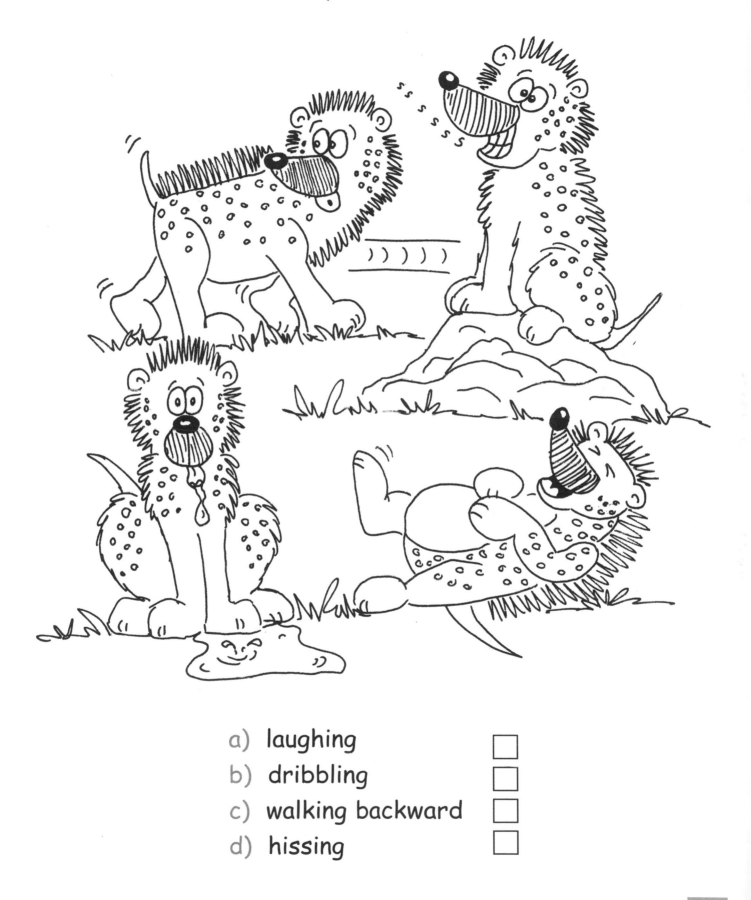

a) laughing ☐
b) dribbling ☐
c) walking backward ☐
d) hissing ☐

# Code names

Here is a code used to enter the names of robots into a computer.
The letters of the alphabet are made up like this:

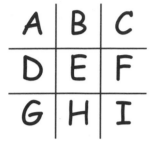  

Using the code, the words **METAL MADNESS** would look like this:

M E T A L    M A D N E S S

Write the coded names of these robots.

R O B O B U G

S O N I C B O O M

H O V E R B O T

W I M B L E B O T

324

# Shepherd's watch

The sheep are scattered, it's getting late and Rex the dog
is not at the gate! Can you see him?

# On the beach

Two people in this scene are going to play a game of tennis.
Can you find them both?

# What's gone wrong?

The artist has drawn some silly things in this picture.
Can you find them?

# Word web

Look at the letters caught in the spider's web.
Unscramble them to reveal a word. Write the word on the line.

_____

# Copy the picture

Use the grid to help you draw the picture, copying square by square.

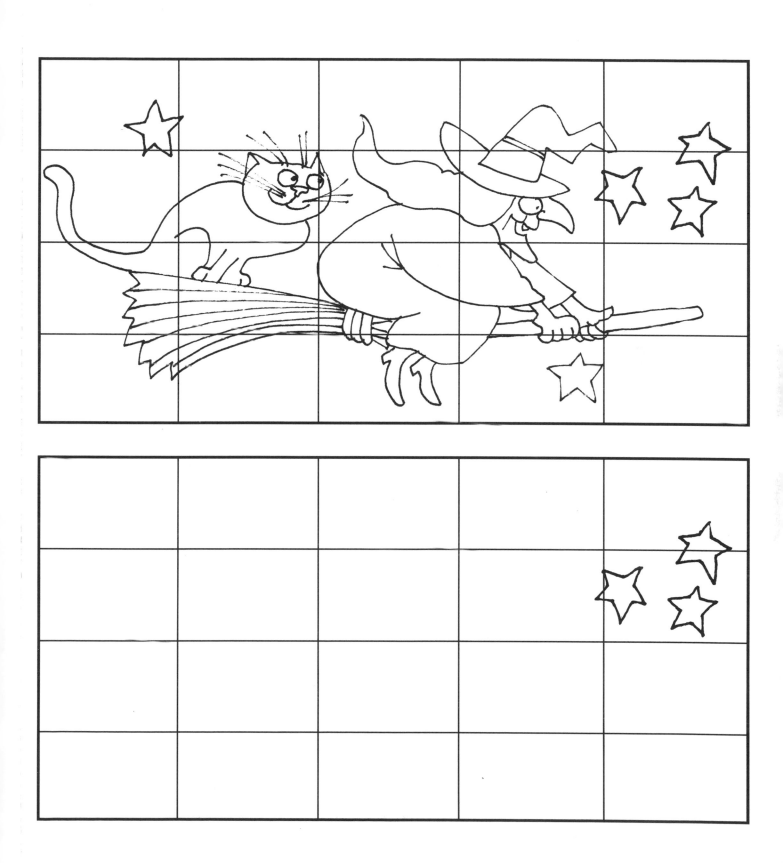

# Robobeast feast

The machine-munching Robobeast is getting hungry.
Draw some metal snacks for it to munch.

# Crossword puzzle

Use the pictures and clues to complete this crossword.
Follow the numbers across and down, and write the words in the grid.

1) Ben is short for which boy's name?
2) If something weighs a lot, it is... ?
3) These are at the ends of your fingers
4) You do this when you are sad
5) You put these in your drink to chill it
6) The opposite of hot

# One out of two

The pictures are clues. By joining the pictures on the left to those on the right, you will make new longer words.
The example will help you.

example:

# Copy and draw...

Use the grid to copy the picture of Sonicboom.
Part of the drawing has been started for you.

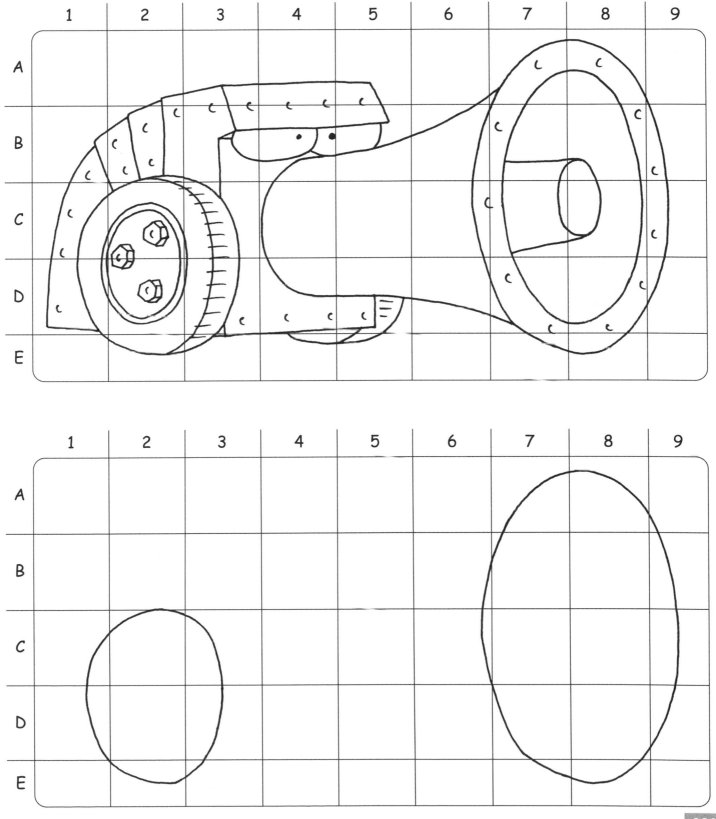

# Puzzle wheel

Write the first letter of each picture in the spaces in the middle of the puzzle wheels.

You will spell one of the shades of the rainbow.

You will spell a name.

# Clothes search

There are seven types of clothes hidden in this grid.
Circle the words as you find them.

| G | K | S | W | E | E | L | M | O |
| S | R | O | X | U | K | M | D | O |
| H | A | T | G | S | O | C | K | S |
| I | M | W | P | H | I | V | Z | A |
| R | F | B | M | O | N | O | P | D |
| T | E | I | Z | E | X | H | O | D |
| A | L | L | T | S | U | S | S | R |
| E | D | Y | I | Q | E | T | I | E |
| H | O | Z | C | M | Q | U | P | S |
| S | J | E | A | N | S | E | R | S |

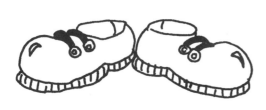

# Dragon's delight

Sir Chitchat is fighting for Arthur's award, but he won't get far without his sword! Can you find it?

# First letters

Look at the pictures and write the first letter of each word
in the grid at the bottom of the page.
Rearrange the letters to spell a word.

# Nature watch

There are five outdoor things hidden in this grid.
Circle the words as you find them.

| P | S | N | A | I | L | Q | E | R |
|---|---|---|---|---|---|---|---|---|
| A | D | G | H | C | E | J | K | Z |
| E | T | Y | D | J | A | F | N | E |
| S | B | W | R | I | F | K | G | K |
| H | P | H | U | Q | N | B | H | R |
| E | U | X | L | N | Q | R | S | A |
| D | T | I | H | E | W | X | E | M |
| D | V | L | Z | S | B | D | F | J |
| S | L | B | O | T | W | Y | G | J |
| U | G | C | U | K | B | I | R | D |

# Muddled machine

This machine has got in a muddle. Match the questions to the answers.

1. How many legs does a fly have?
answer: DODO

2. What is the highest mountain in the world?
answer: SLEEPING

3. Whose flag features a red maple leaf?
answer: 6

4. Which extinct bird lived on the island of Mauritius?
answer: 12 O'CLOCK

5. Name the largest meat-eating dinosaur.
answer: EVEREST

6. What is the capital city of France?
answer: CANADA

7. What time is at midnight?
answer: T-REX

8. What are sloths well-known for?
answer: PARIS

# Hidden wands

The witches and wizards have taken some time off for a break
by the sea. Unfortunately, they have lost some wands.
How many are hidden in the picture?
Write the number in the box.

Number of wands

# Hidden word

Cross out the letters that appear twice in the grid.
The letters that are left spell a boy's name.
Write your answer on the line below.

| D | J | I | Z | W |
|---|---|---|---|---|
| T | G | U | Q | A |
| M | Q | O | E | H |
| H | O | G | D | T |
| I | W | Z | S | U |

# Word trail

Use the picture clues to fill in the word trail.
The last letter of each word is the first of the next word.

# Snow good!

The snowman was happy the kids were keeping him snug.
He wished he had arms to give them a hug! Can you find him a hat?

# Which way to win?

Guide the robot to the trophy.

# Number puzzle

Add the missing numbers to complete the grid.

| 7 | + | 3 | = |   |
|---|---|---|---|---|
| − | ■ | − | ■ | − |
|   | + | 0 | = | 2 |
| = | ■ | = | ■ | = |
| 5 | + |   | = | 8 |

# Telephone differences

These three spies are listening in to someone's telephone call.
Can you find the differences between the two pictures?

# Most and fewest

Who has the most spiders and who has the fewest?
Count the spiders and write the answers on the cauldrons.

# Whose shoes?

The witches and wizards have mixed up their shoes.
Follow the lines to match the shoes to the right owners.

# Quiz **time**

In which country is Table Mountain?

a) Spain ☐
b) Australia ☐
c) France ☐
d) South Africa ☐

# Beanstalk **blunder**

In his hurry, Jack believes, his harp was dropped in the beanstalk's leaves.
Can you find it?

# Shadow search

Which shadow matches the picture in the box exactly?

# How many squares?

Look carefully at this picture.
How many squares can you see altogether?
Be careful, some are hidden!

# Program puzzle

This is a code used to program robots with instructions:

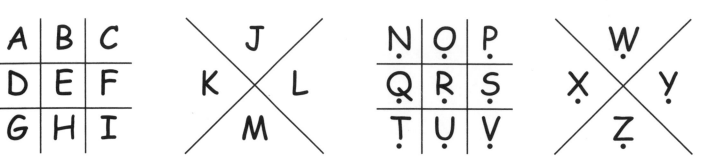

Using the code, the words HEAVY METAL would look like this:

Can you work out what these coded messages say?

354

# Gnasher

Use the grid to copy the picture of Gnasher.
Part of the drawing has been started for you.

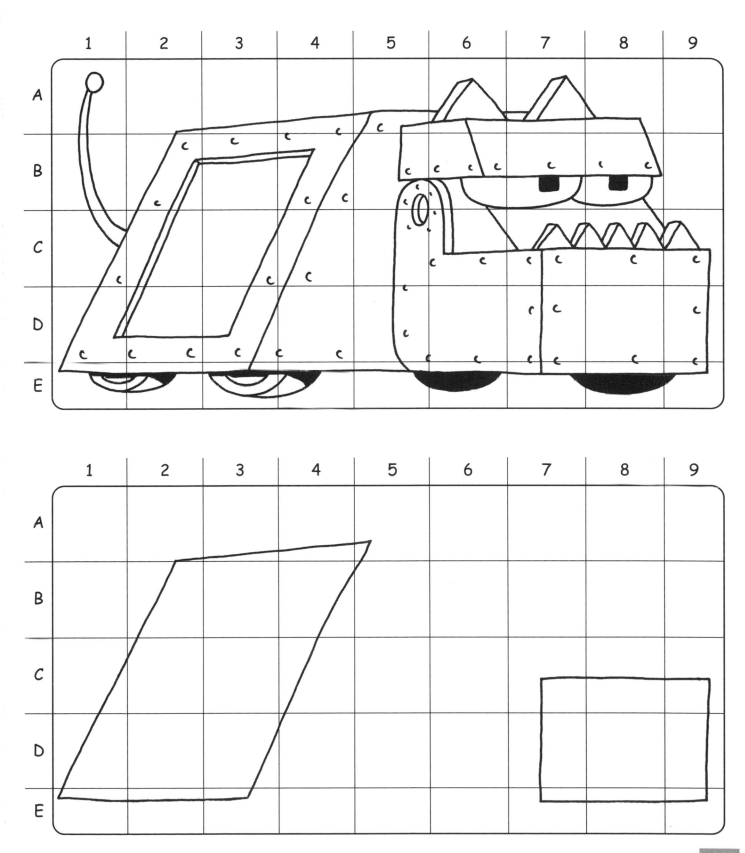

# In the city

The pictures are clues and the numbers show you where each word goes in the grid. Write the words in the crossword.

# Do you know?

The questions on this page have been muddled up.
See if you can match the questions to the correct pictures.
Write the answers on the lines.

1 You write with this.

_____

2 The opposite of closed.

_____

3 These fall from trees.

_____

4 This is where bees live.

_____

# Quiz time

What type of fish are threshers and hammerheads?

a) sharks ☐
b) crabs ☐
c) whales ☐
d) seals ☐

# Puzzle **cobweb**

Write the first letter of each picture in the spaces in the middle of the cobweb. Unscramble the letters to spell the name of something wizards make.

# Welcome robots

Both these pictures may look the same, but there are eight differences, so look again!
Circle the differences as you find them.

# Pets' names

Draw a line from each animal to the name you think it should have.

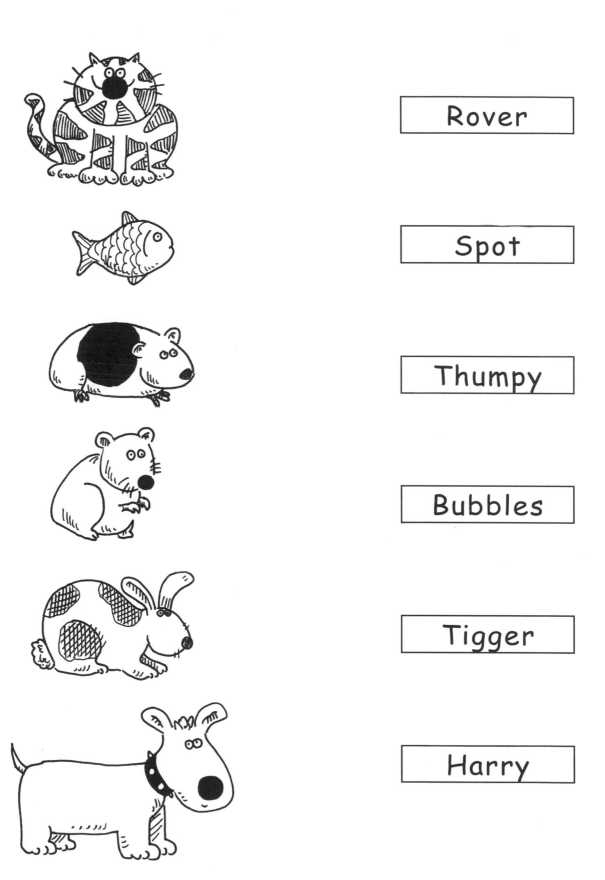

Rover

Spot

Thumpy

Bubbles

Tigger

Harry

# Number sudoku

This puzzle is a 4 x 4 grid of boxes in which you need to put four sets of numbers: 1, 2, 3, 4. Each number must appear once in each row, once in each column, and once in each 2 x 2 box. If any number appears twice in the same box, row or column, you have to start all over again!

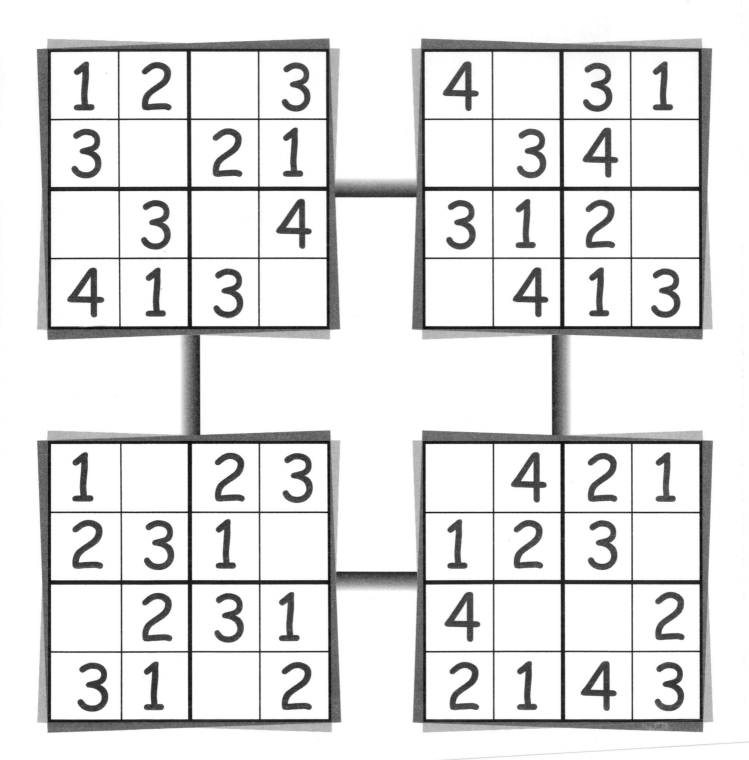

# Troublesome tunnels

Help the mole find his way out of the underground maze.

# Odd **bot** out

These six pictures of Wingdemon may look the same, but one of them is slightly different. Can you work out which one it is?

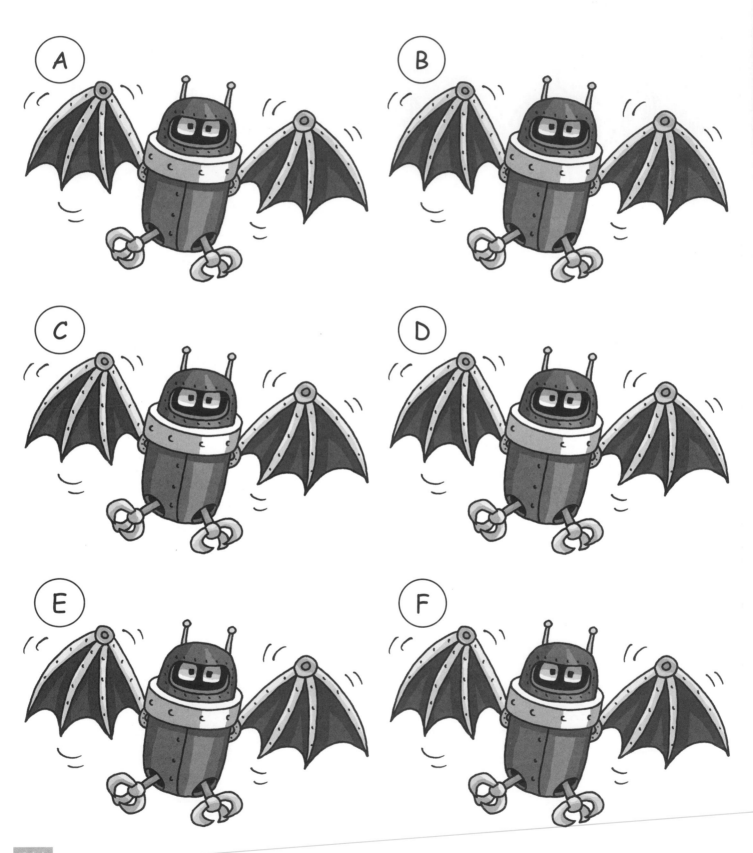

# Quiz time

What type of insect is a painted lady?

a) a beetle ☐
b) a butterfly ☐
c) a spider ☐
d) a wasp ☐

# Marine garden

Both these pictures may look the same, but there are
eight differences, so look again!
Circle the differences as you find them.

# Kitten capers

Use the coded key to find out what this sentence says.

KQTTJNS LQKJ TS
DRQNK MQLK FND
PLFY WQTH BFLLS
SF WSSL.

**Key**

A = F
E = J
I = Q
O = S
U = Z

# Pattern **sudoku**

This puzzle is a 4 x 4 grid of boxes in which you need to put four patterns. Each pattern must appear once in each row, once in each column, and once in each 2 x 2 box. If any pattern appears twice in the same box, row or column, you have to start all over again!

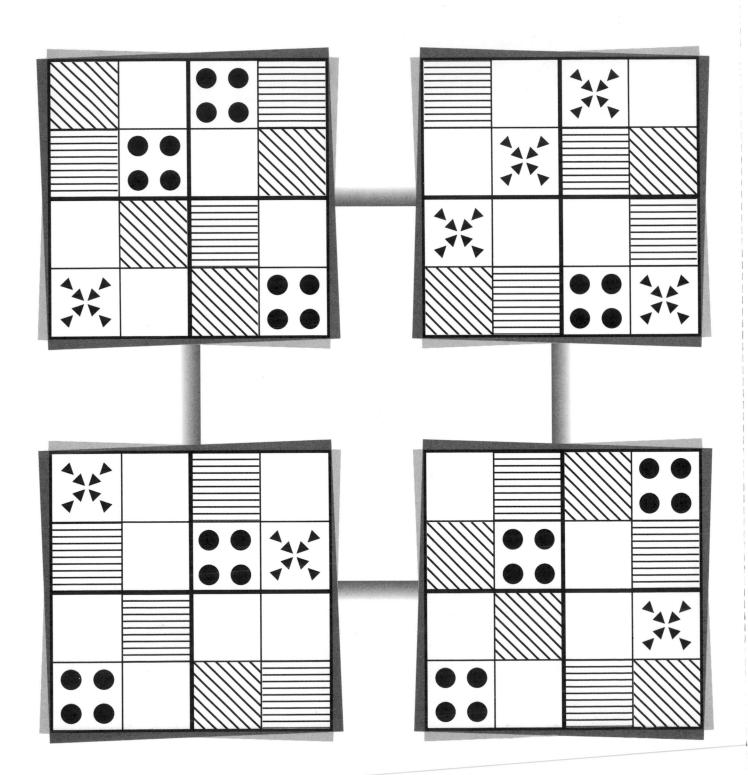

# Suitable cases

Which two suitcases are identical? Draw a line to match the pair.

# Roald Dahl story search

Find the words listed below. Words can go horizontally, vertically, and diagonally. They can read forward and backward.

```
L M B O R A U I T Q H R T W R F R J G H
Y R U Y N Z D Y P E A N H H D B J Z X V
B J Y S K H T V E N P K P E E A L Q V L
B J J B V C U F Y O M V E S B T N F F Q
O M N I W K J A D R O W T I W Z W N N C
W D K G R A D N V M O R E O H H C I Y I
A A Z F C R I T I O L C K T C C K S T X
U M O R E I E A C U H E C R W A B W Z S
G I Q I A N V S N S A A U O D E A P U F
U K V E D R I T G C P D B T L P M Q M K
S E E N G N N I I R M G E M A T Z Z L W
T T R D C C I C X O O C I D S N V N K A
U E W L B C C M M C O B L N U A P J D U
S E I Y Z A B R B O L Z R D N I C L J Y
G V T G L Y D F W D I L A L N G I O P I
L E C I Q H I O Z I N Q H X I T Y M F Y
O E H A Q Q L X E L W Q C V A M L T E R
O A E N H D L C P E D H Y M C V Y A G X
P E S T C H O C O L A T E F A C T O R Y
W I L L Y W O N K A M R Z S W O W H Y G
```

| | | |
|---|---|---|
| AUGUSTUS GLOOP | ESIO TROT | THE TWITS |
| BIG FRIENDLY GIANT | FANTASTIC MR FOX | WILLY WONKA |
| CHARLIE BUCKET | GIANT PEACH | WITCHES |
| CHOCOLATE FACTORY | MATILDA | |
| DANNY | MIKE TEEVEE | |
| ENORMOUS CROCODILE | OOMPAH LOOMPAH | |

# Treasure island

The map shows the places where pirates might have hidden their treasure, but parts of the names are missing.
Fill in the missing letters.

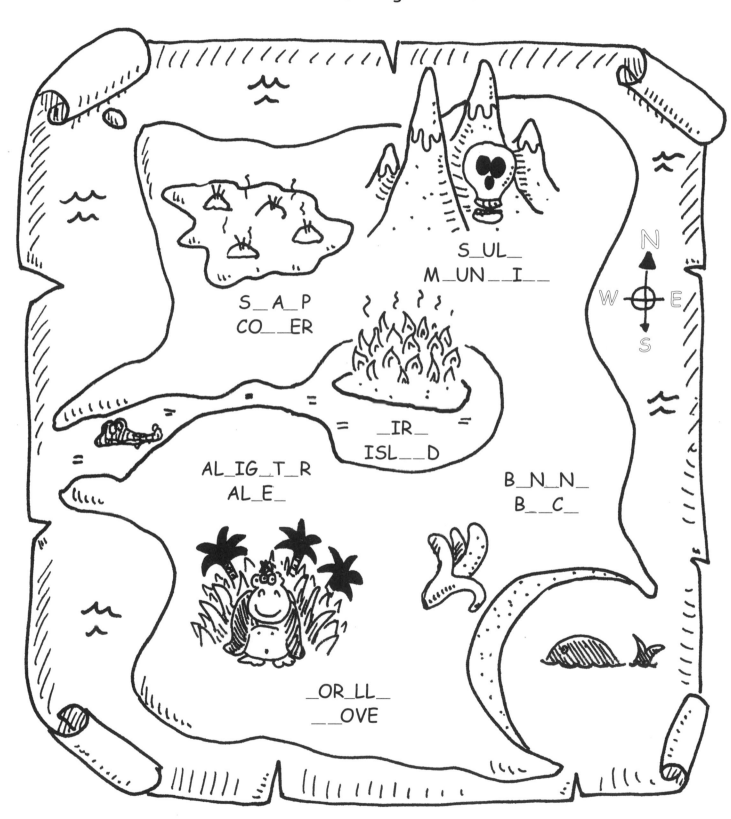

S_UL_
M_UN__I__

S_ _A_P
CO_ _ER

_IR_
ISL_ _D

AL_IG_T_R
AL_E_

B_N_N_
B_ _C_

_OR_LL_
_ _OVE

N
W   E
S

# Quiz time

What is the fastest land animal?

a) horse ☐
b) cheetah ☐
c) dog ☐
d) tortoise ☐

# King of the castle

Both these pictures may look the same, but there are eight differences, so look again! Circle the differences as you find them.

# Where and when?

Use the coded key to find out what this message says.

THSSS CHNLDRSN
DRS MSSTNNG
ANDSR THS CLWCK
DT TWW W'CLWCK.

Key

A = D
E = S
I = N
O = W
U = A

# Animal sudoku

This puzzle is a 4 x 4 grid of boxes in which you need to put four animals: fish, butterfly, sheep, cat. Each animal must appear once in each row, once in each column, and once in each 2 x 2 box. If any animal appears twice in the same box, row or column, you have to start all over again!

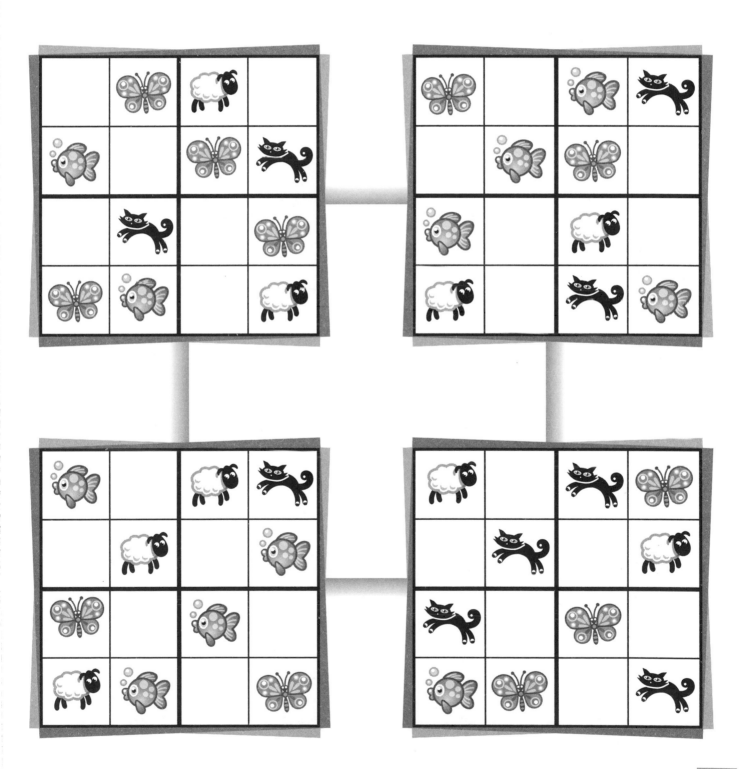

# Crossed words

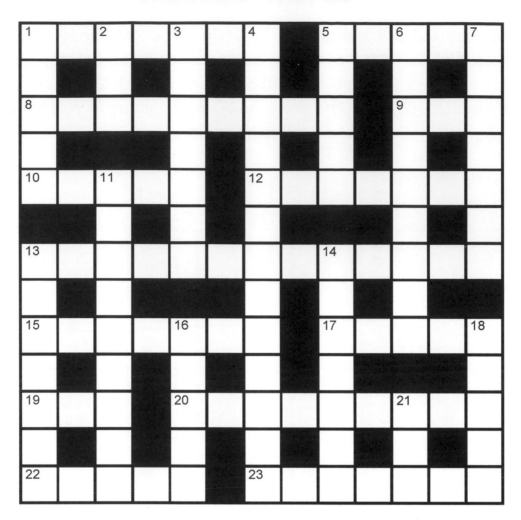

**Across**

1) Heirs to the throne (7)

5) Wrist clock (5)

8) Interrupted (9)

9) ___ away means to recede (3)

10) Sri ___, name for the country formerly known as Ceylon (5)

12) Overseas postal service (3,4)

13) The force surrounding a moving charged particle (8,5)

15) Small, simple house in the country (7)

17) Raw fish, as eaten in Japan (5)

19) ___ constrictor, large snake (3)

20) Nurserymen (9)

22) Foe (5)

23) Electrical power (7)

**Down**

1) Accelerator on a bicycle! (5)

2) ___ and buts are excuses (3)

3) Bravery (7)

4) Sailors on a U-boat (9,4)

5) Less narrow (5)

6) Adolescents (9)

7) Limped (7)

11) Bad dream (9)

13) Gruesome (7)

14) Quickest (7)

16) Annoyed (5)

18) Important question (5)

21) Extended time period (3)

# Twice the fun

The pictures are clues to the crossword.
When you have completed the grid, unscramble the letters in the
shaded boxes to spell a new word.

# Rattlebones!

Both these pictures may look the same, but there are eight differences, so look again! Circle the differences as you find them.

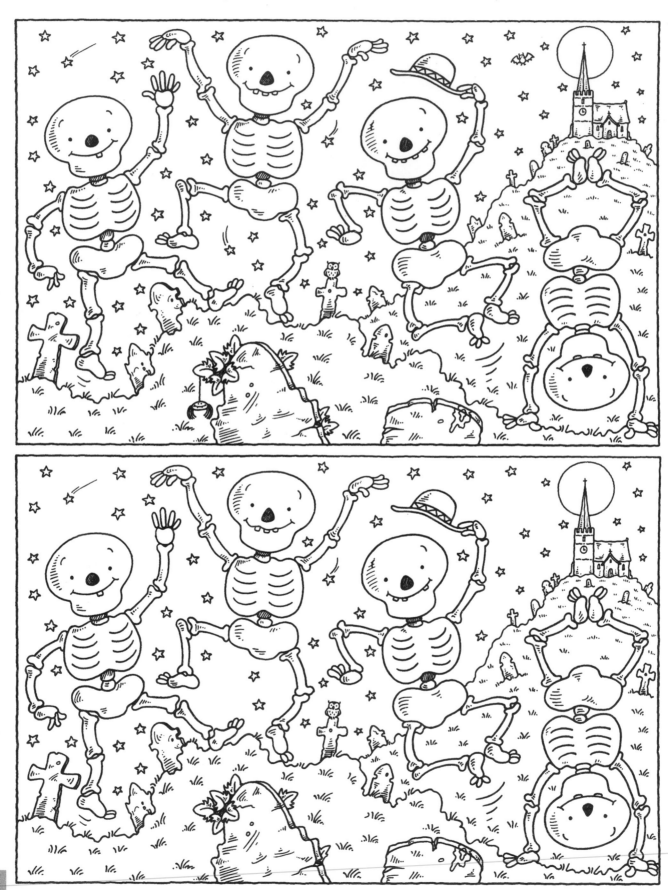

# Picture search

Write the names of the objects in the spaces beneath them.
Can you find these words in the grid?
You can read them in any direction.

| B | C | H | C | G | E | N | T | U | T |
|---|---|---|---|---|---|---|---|---|---|
| O | O | A | I | H | G | H | I | U | X |
| L | S | L | N | F | A | B | I | N | N |
| R | P | E | T | N | A | I | G | S | P |
| E | A | W | H | E | E | L | N | E | Q |
| N | N | S | P | A | N | C | F | A | R |
| N | P | Y | D | E | P | E | R | T | S |
| A | Y | Y | D | T | E | R | S | U | P |
| P | B | E | N | G | I | N | E | P | J |
| S | O | N | U | K | P | A | R | G | L |

W _ _ _ _ _

E _ _ _ _ _ _

C _ _ _ _ _

B _ _ _

S _ _ _ _

S _ _ _ _ _ _ _

N _ _

# Quiz time

Which is the largest of the cat family?

a) puma ☐
b) panther ☐
c) leopard ☐
d) tiger ☐

# Disguises

The pictures are clues. Look for these words in the grid.
You will find them by reading across or down.
Circle the words as you find them.

```
M  C  A  F  H  A  T  Q  J
A  P  W  B  S  B  K  G  L
G  L  A  R  O  D  Y  L  I
N  F  Z  I  Q  C  O  A  T
I  R  G  E  G  Q  R  S  O
F  V  E  F  A  U  G  S  G
Y  R  B  C  K  H  L  E  L
I  R  L  A  S  P  D  S  A
N  Q  N  S  K  R  A  M  S
G  C  B  E  A  R  D  X  S
```

# Animal sudoku

This puzzle is a 4 x 4 grid of boxes in which you need to put four animals: fish, butterfly, sheep, cat. Each animal must appear once in each row, once in each column, and once in each 2 x 2 box. If any animal appears twice in the same box, row or column, you have to start all over again!

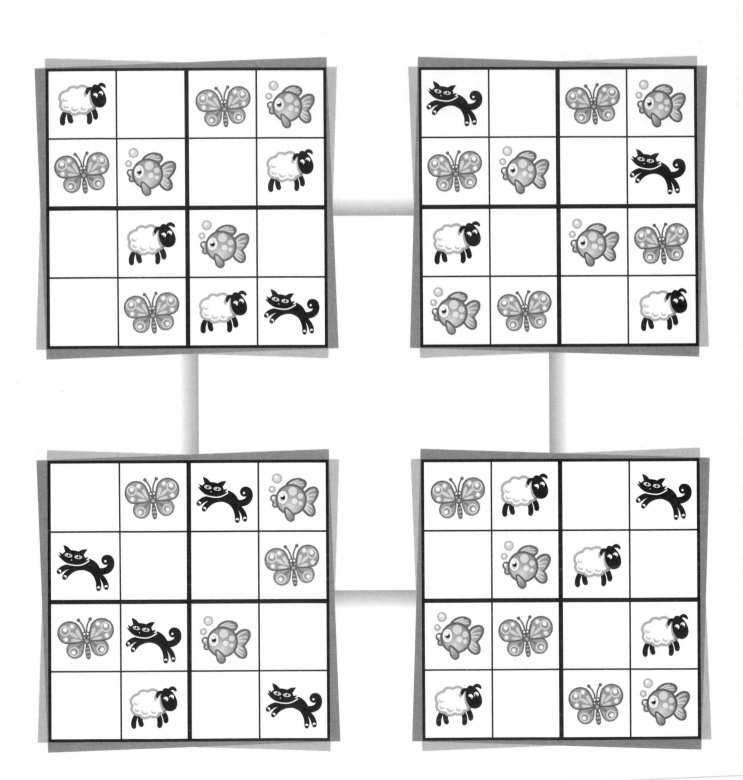

# Underwater search

Find the words listed below. Words can go horizontally, vertically, and diagonally. They can read forward and backward.

```
L E V R C X K I Y K X Z B E D M W K G B
X M Z K S D C E T T T N O V E M F I X Y
W I X R K A S R U G U D A Z V W G W L E
I K A A U L L C A N Y W I O Q D Y K T N
H V Q H K W O M U B Z X Z A O V D Y O O
T S Q S S H L B O B H S I F R A T S O M
G T O E H A Z F S N A S P A H L E C A E
P I W M I L J K J T E D S W H A T M C N
O N J H P E K L P A E E I X X O W Z W A
R G J M W Z Z U B S A R F V P O C X X B
E R D P R C X E S H L E L U E L H A K E
T A T D E A D H O S V Y S R O R A H E Q
S Y R R C T O R A R P M D W S Z Q Y B I
Y A O E K A S O X S J W N L Q F U H M O
O R U F L E M H Y K X F N O T K N A L P
B T T N S C Z E P J I S H V P J Y V E E
B L U E T A N G C S S U C T E V G T O D
P J K U R E V Q H J U O I A W M O J E L
W I D S F E E R L A R O C I J M N C B M
W K Z S S F H C R O P L E E Y A R O M P
```

| | | | |
|---|---|---|---|
| ANEMONE | LOBSTER | SCUBA DIVER | STARFISH |
| BLUE TANG | MORAY EEL | SEA HORSE | STING RAY |
| CLOWNFISH | OCTOPUS | SEABED | TROUT |
| CORAL REEF | OYSTER | SHARK | WHALE |
| CRAB | PLANKTON | SHIPWRECK | |
| HAKE | SALMON | SHOAL | |

# Tell the **time**

Can you crack this letter code to find out the question?
Write the answer on the lines.

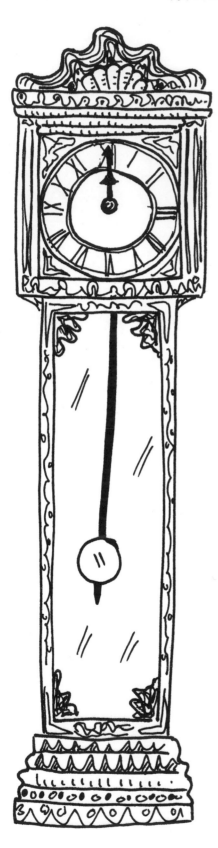

WHA TTI MEI
SMIDD AY?

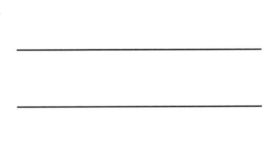

_____

_____

_____

# Number **puzzle**

Fill in the numbers to complete the grid.

| 2 | + |   | = | 10 |
| - | ■ | - | ■ | - |
|   | + | 2 | = | 3 |
| = | ■ | = | ■ | = |
| 1 | + | 6 | = |   |

# Snoozing in the savannah

Can you see the snoozing crocodile?

# Safe and sound

Which of these things will help you keep a spy camp secure?
Put ticks in the boxes.

# Quiz time

How many sets of teeth do most mammals have?

a) 3  ☐
b) 2  ☐
c) 6  ☐
d) 1  ☐

# Two into one

The pictures are clues. By connecting the pictures on the left to those on the right, you will make new longer words. The example will help you.

example:

# Shadow search

Which shadow matches the picture in the box exactly?

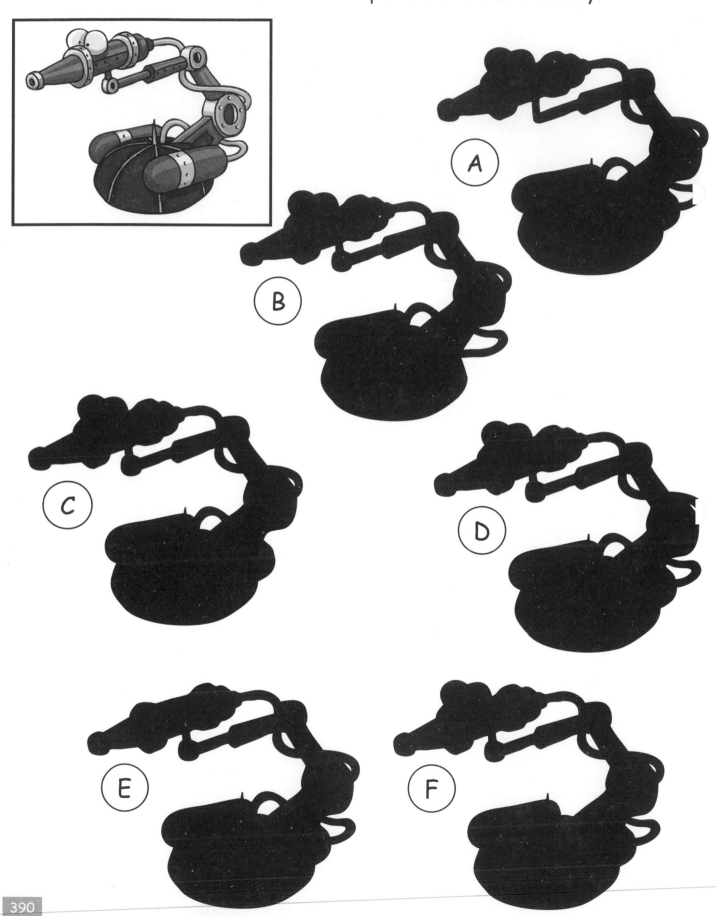

# Nuts **and** bolts

How many nuts and bolts can you count in this picture?

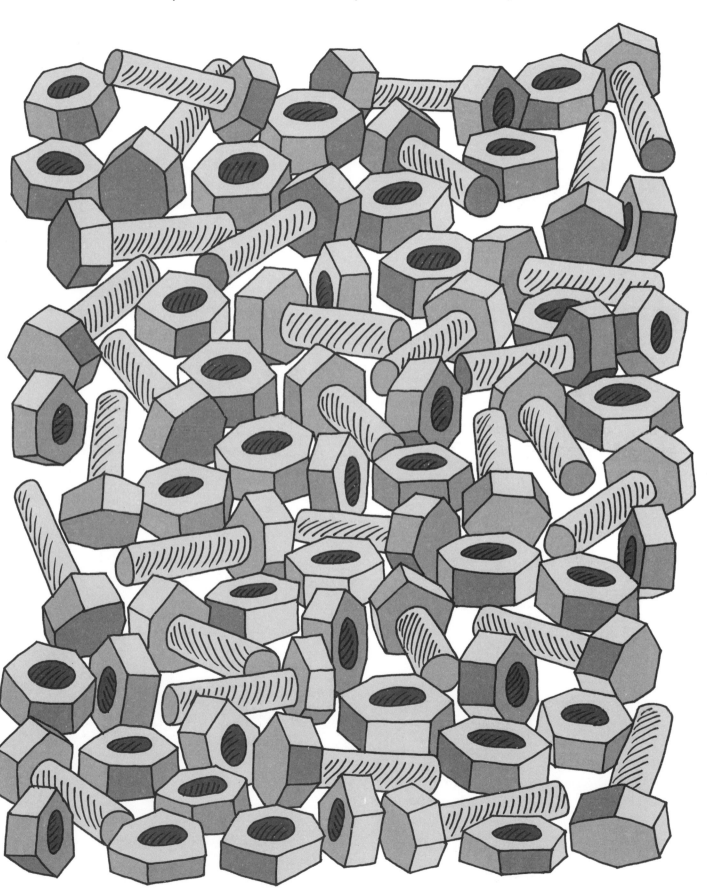

# Number sudoku

This puzzle is a 4 x 4 grid of boxes in which you need to put four sets of numbers: 1, 2, 3, 4. Each number must appear once in each row, once in each column, and once in each 2 x 2 box. If any number appears twice in the same box, row or column, you have to start all over again!

# In search of numbers

Fill in the numbers to complete the grid.

| 9 | + |   | = | 11 |
|---|---|---|---|----|
| + | ■ | + | ■ | − |
| 5 | − | 3 | = |   |
| = | ■ | = | ■ | = |
|   | − | 5 | = | 9 |

# Monkey's mate

It's monkey's turn to find his friend, but he is sad and wants the game to end! Can you find his friend?

# Quiz time

What do beavers build?

a) dams ☐
b) nests ☐
c) bridges ☐
d) towers ☐

# Washed and ready

The pictures are clues. Look for the words in the grid.
You will find them by reading across or down.
Circle the words as you find them.

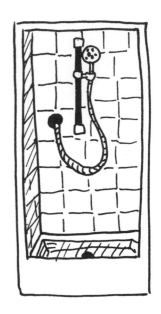

| Q | B | E | A | K | E | R | J | F |
|---|---|---|---|---|---|---|---|---|
| V | A | G | G | I | L | J | M | N |
| F | T | O | I | L | E | T | J | B |
| R | H | F | I | Y | B | F | L | G |
| T | G | Y | S | H | O | W | E | R |
| O | T | O | P | S | F | C | U | S |
| W | Y | U | O | O | I | L | E | W |
| E | D | C | N | R | P | H | U | Q |
| L | Z | T | G | U | R | N | L | L |
| W | X | H | E | P | Y | K | S | N |

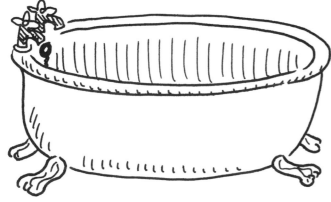

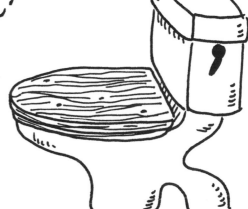

# Egyptian dot-to-dot

Starting at number 1, connect the dots to complete the picture.

# Harry Potter word puzzle

Find the words listed below. Words can go horizontally, vertically, and diagonally, and can read forward and backward.

```
C G H I P E E X G K U F C J I P Y T O R
A X N C P A F H A U S T A N G N A O B Y
O L I P T H M F U V A L J R U H B M S O
Q D H E R I O S F O P F Y E L D U D O I
H B D A H C D E R I F F O T E L B O G K
Z U S M G U Q D N E F O H T H K D E M F
B X N Y W R R W I I D F Z O E E B N O W
I P J B I W I G N U X U C P G S R O J L
F Q A G M P D D M R Q L A Y I W N I N Y
E L N Z X D O B O B O N Q R R V A M N X
C H G P N R L S Z E S V I R A N B R U M
M U B S B E S I X C W U O A E M A E T X
K F A X D E D A E M S G O H K V K H J S
J F Y O F L A M U B U E I O E L Z G U P
L L R O P R Y E L S A E W N O R A V X F
S E R X Q B X A P L P L C Z H S F E U P
W P X Z N D C O H V O L X Y U C B S N O
P U F P E K R L F D A F I I A V A Z E B
A F C N U R N N Y W P Q D T Q H Z Q E U
F F G L R L K S K C I P O H S B B Z B T
```

AZKABAN
DUDLEY
DUMBLEDORE
GOBLET OF FIRE
GRYFFINDOR
HAGRID

HARRY POTTER
HERMIONE
HOGSMEADE
HOGWARTS
HUFFLEPUFF
MALFOY

MARAUDERS
MAP
PHOENIX
PROFESSOR
QUIDDITCH
RAVENCLAW

RON WEASLEY
SIRIUS BLACK
SLYTHERIN
SNAPE

# Letter sudoku

This puzzle is a 4 x 4 grid of boxes in which you need to put four sets of letters: X, G, M, A. Each letter must appear once in each row, once in each column, and once in each 2 x 2 box. If any letter appears twice in the same box, row, or column, you have to start all over again!

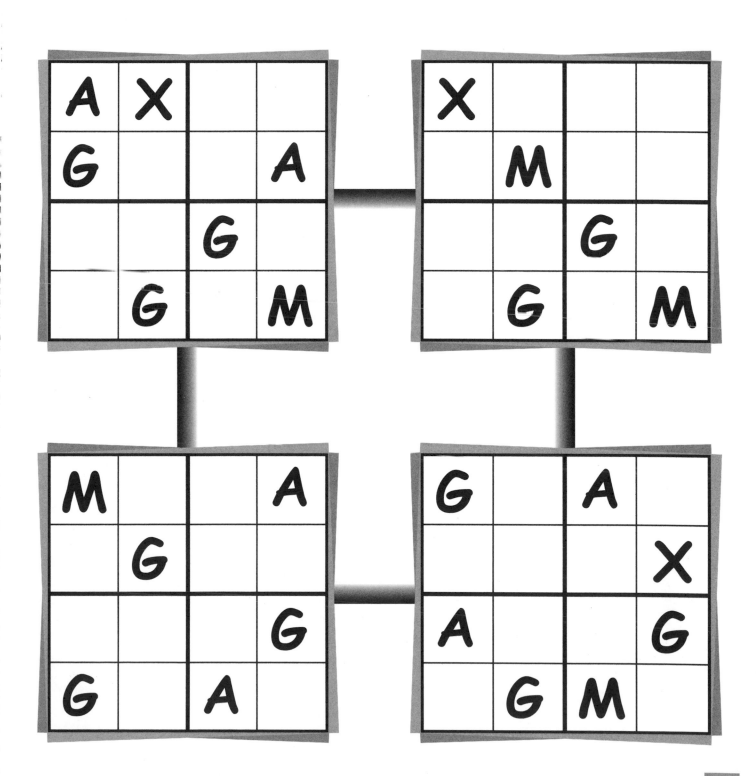

# In a **jam**

A good secret agent will be able to see the things that are wrong with this picture. Can you find them all?

# Sudoku

To solve this puzzle, every number from 1 to 9 must appear in each of the nine vertical columns, in each of the nine horizontal rows, and in each of the nine boxes.

| | | | | 8 | 2 | 5 | | |
|---|---|---|---|---|---|---|---|---|
| | 5 | 6 | | 3 | 4 | | 8 | |
| 8 | | 7 | | | | 3 | 9 | |
| 7 | 1 | | 6 | | 8 | | | |
| 3 | 6 | | | | | | 2 | 8 |
| | | | 3 | | 5 | | 1 | 9 |
| | 2 | 4 | | | | 9 | | 1 |
| | 7 | | 2 | 9 | | 8 | 6 | |
| | | 8 | 4 | 1 | | | | |

# Sports crossword

The pictures are clues and the numbers show you where each word goes in the grid. Write the words in the crossword.

# Picture sudoku

This puzzle is a 6 x 6 grid of boxes in which you need to put six sets of symbols: fox, cat, cheese, tree, chicken, teapot. Each picture must appear once in each row, once in each column, and once in each 3 x 2 box. If any picture appears twice in the same box, row, or column, you have to start all over again!

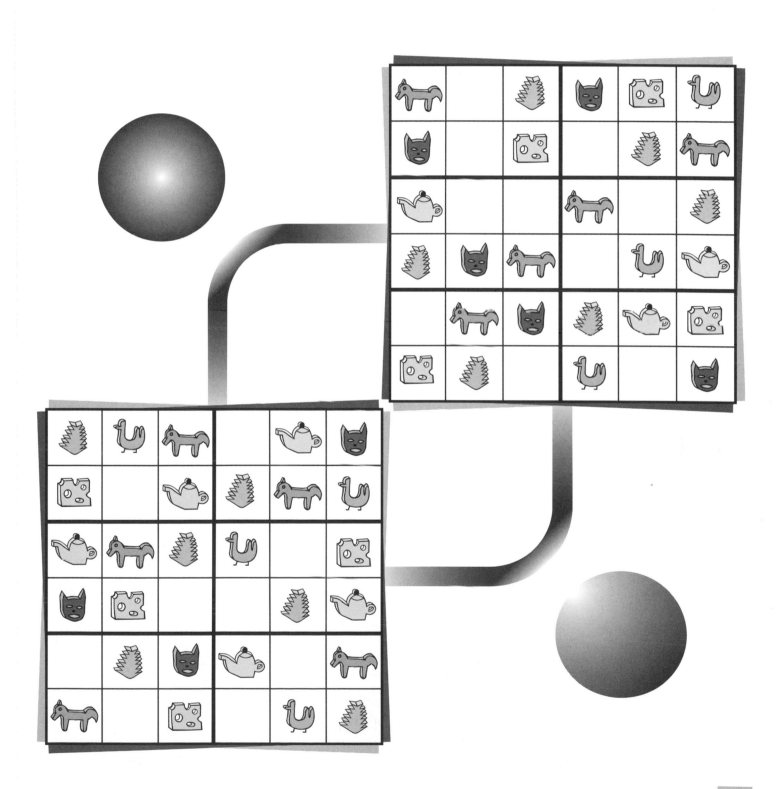

# Daydreamer

This boy is reading a book about a castle.
Draw what you think the castle looks like.

# Half and half

Complete the picture by drawing the missing half.

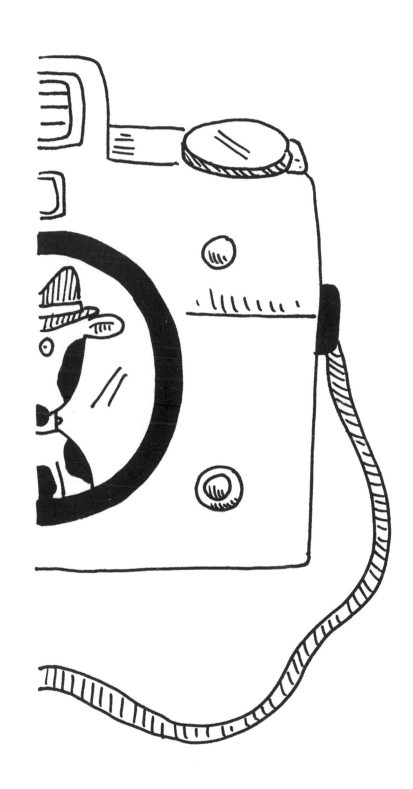

# Sudoku

To solve this puzzle, every number from 1 to 9 must appear in each
of the nine vertical columns, in each of the nine horizontal rows,
and in each of the nine boxes.

| 9 |   |   |   |   | 8 | 7 |   | 2 |
|---|---|---|---|---|---|---|---|---|
|   | 4 |   | 1 | 3 |   |   | 8 |   |
| 8 |   | 6 | 9 |   |   | 5 |   |   |
| 4 |   |   | 7 |   | 5 | 3 | 9 |   |
|   | 5 |   |   |   |   |   | 2 |   |
|   | 9 | 8 | 4 |   | 6 |   |   | 7 |
|   |   | 4 |   |   | 1 | 9 |   | 5 |
|   | 8 |   |   | 6 | 4 |   | 3 |   |
| 1 |   | 5 | 2 |   |   |   |   | 8 |

# Family word puzzle

Find the words listed below. Words can go horizontally, vertically, and diagonally, and can read forward and backward.

```
P X A W B M O T H E R Y P Y G
H Y B N I S U O C H H X M D T
B P J R Y H H K E I B S Y O P
N V Y R R N M Q A G Y C L I V
W X G Y A E B A R W E H P E N
Q W I N T L O A U N J T Q Z A
N T N D H Q N X Z A L U Q B N
A A W L S D P E U H U X R R Q
F C T I A V W E J Z Z N S Z N
A Y A D B R O T H E R I T I X
T Z H M N U Q C D B S W E I P
H U X A U N V U T C C O R E
E B A B Y E N C E P E Q P J V
R W N L N O A R L K C E Z K M
P Q M R L U E V C E A O D P U
```

AUNTIE     FATHER     NEPHEW
BABY     GRANDAD     NIECE
BROTHER     MOTHER     SISTER
COUSIN     NANNA     UNCLE

# Pretty puzzle

Fill in the answers to the problems to complete the grid.

| 3 | + | 6 | = | |
|---|---|---|---|---|
| + | █ | − | █ | − |
| 2 | + | | = | 6 |
| = | █ | = | █ | = |
| | − | 2 | = | 3 |

# In good shape!

This puzzle is a 4 x 4 grid of boxes in which you need to put four sets of shapes: ▲★■● . Each shape must appear once in each row, once in each column, and once in each 2 x 2 box. If any shape appears twice in the same box, row or column, you have to start all over again!

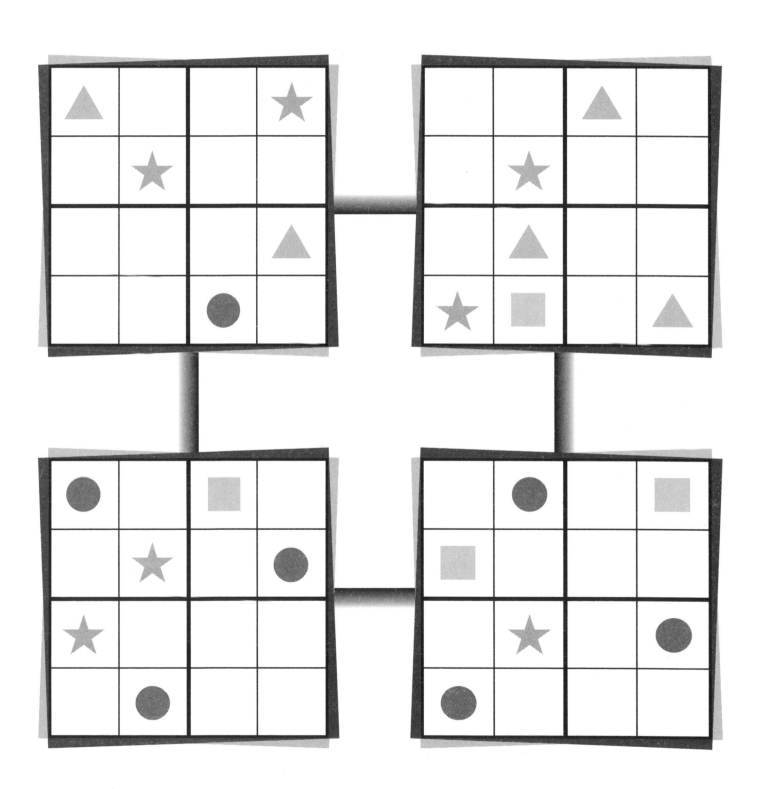

# Eye spy

List the things you can spy in this picture that begin with the letter **b**.

_____

_____

_____

_____

# Bank note

Design a new bank note. Which country would it be for?
How much would it be worth? Remember to design both sides.

# Count on me!

This puzzle is a 6 x 6 grid of boxes in which you need to put six sets of numbers: 1,2,3,4,5,6. Each number must appear once in each row, once in each column, and once in each 3 x 2 box. If any number appears twice in the same box, row or column, you have to start all over again!

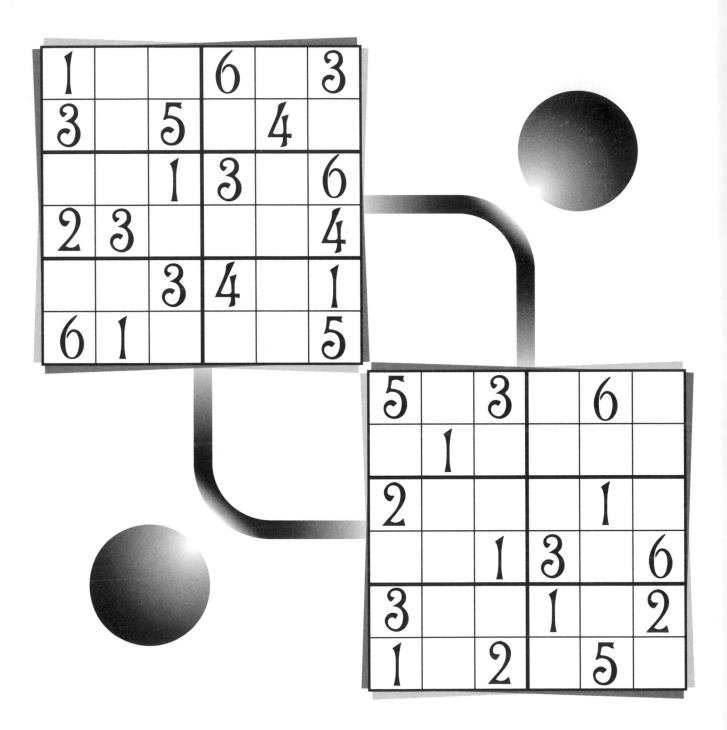

# Which one?

One of these spies has been spotted at the park.
The spy did not have a beard or hat and was not wearing a scarf.
Do you know which spy it was?

# Picture sudoku

This puzzle is a 6 x 6 grid of boxes in which you need to put six pictures: . Each picture must appear once in each row, once in each column, and once in each 3 x 2 box. If any picture appears twice in the same box, row or column, you have to start all over again!

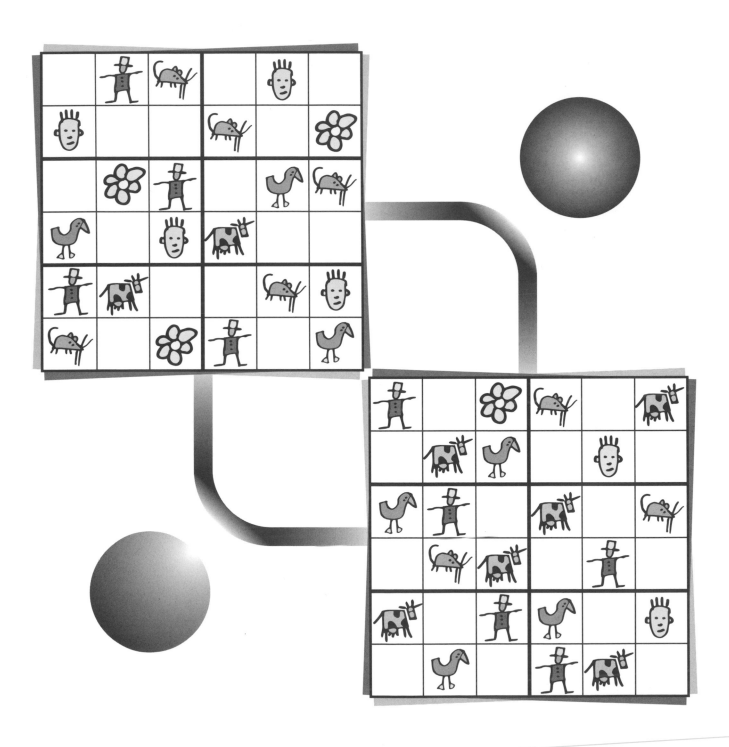

# Princess Xarg

Rock Starjet is here to welcome Princess Xarg aboard the space station. What will she look like? Draw the princess in the teleportation chamber.

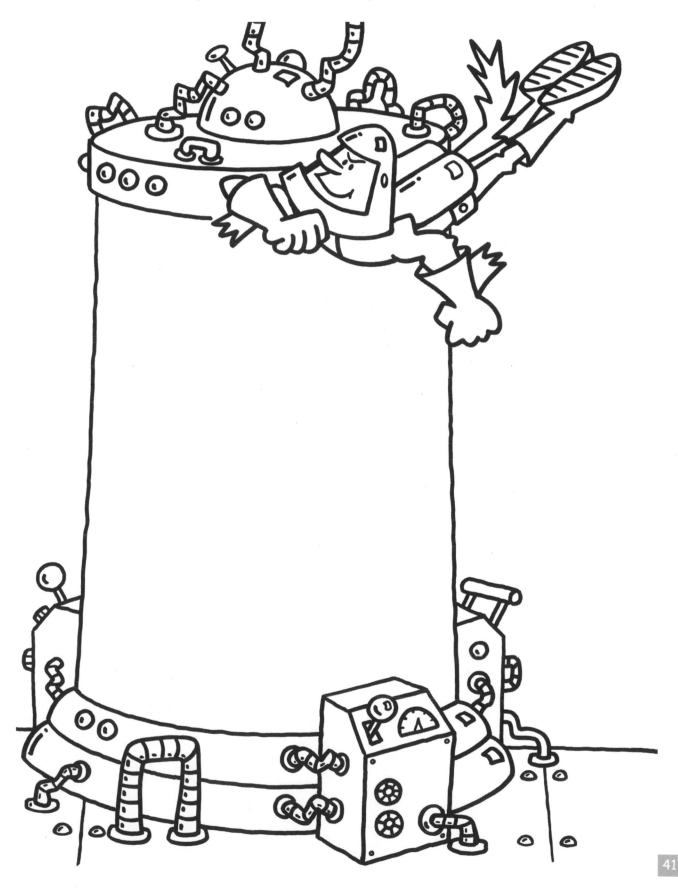

# Problem puzzle

Fill in the answers to the problems to complete the grid.

|     | −   | 5   | =   | 10  |
|-----|-----|-----|-----|-----|
| −   | ■   | −   | ■   | −   |
| 11  | −   |     | =   | 7   |
| =   | ■   | =   | ■   | =   |
| 4   | −   | 1   | =   |     |

# Picture sudoku

This puzzle is a 6 x 6 grid of boxes in which you need to put six sets of symbols: fox, cat, cheese, tree, chicken, teapot. Each picture must appear once in each row, once in each column, and once in each 3 x 2 box. If any picture appears twice in the same box, row or column, you have to start all over again!

# Weather report!

The pictures are clues for the crossword. When you have done the crossword, unscramble the letters in the shaded parts to spell a new word.

# Crossword challenge

**Across**

1) Break free (6)

4) Cutter of men's hair (6)

9) Authorisation (7)

10) "The ___", epic poem about Troy (5)

11) Latin-American dance (5)

12) Flier (7)

13) Capital of Argentina (6,5)

18) Loss of memory (7)

20) Ski slope (5)

22) Shipment of goods (5)

23) Army helicopter (7)

24) Ancient Greek city, home of Oedipus (6)

25) Structural supports (6)

**Down**

1) Hostility (6)

2) Body of accepted rules (5)

3) Vietnam movie starring Charlie Sheen (7)

5) Excuse (5)

6) Easily broken (7)

7) Jockeys (6)

8) Period of European history around the 15th century (11)

14) Frighten (7)

15) Currently published (2,5)

16) Wealthy or overpaid person (3,3)

17) Harmless lizards (6)

19) Hard middle of a fruit (5)

21) Venue for the 1988 Olympic Games (5)

# Number sudoku

This puzzle is a 4 x 4 grid of boxes in which you need to put four sets of numbers: 1,2,3,4. Each number must appear once in each row, once in each column, and once in each 2 x 2 box. If any number appears twice in the same box, row or column, you have to start all over again!

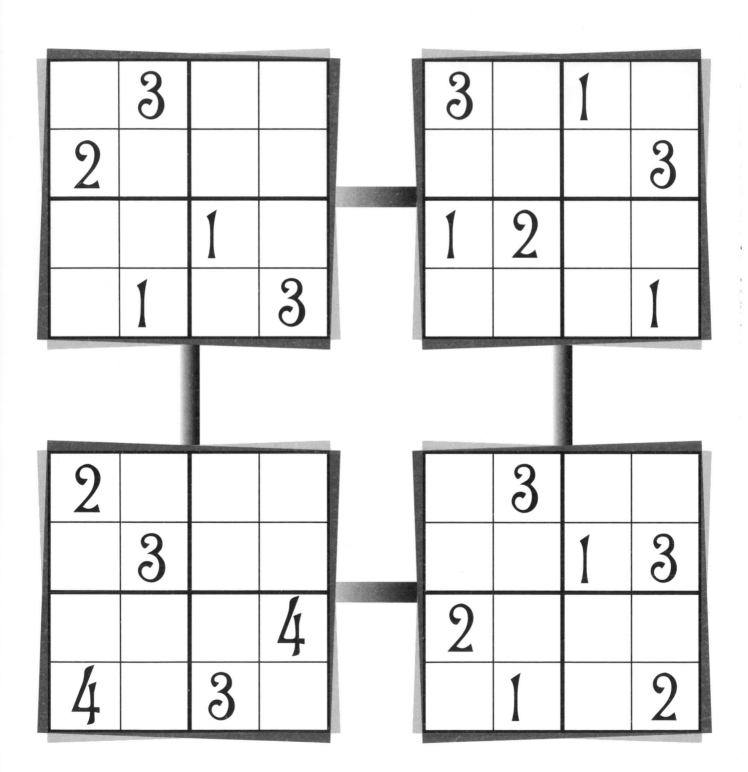

# Present time!

Can you guess what is wrapped up in each parcel?
Write your answers on the lines.

_____

_____

_____

_____

# Six in a fix!

This puzzle is a 6 x 6 grid of boxes in which you need to put six pictures: crab, ship, computer, cow, pencil, cake. Each picture must appear once in each row, once in each column, and once in each 3 x 2 box. If any picture appears twice in the same box, row or column, you have to start all over again!

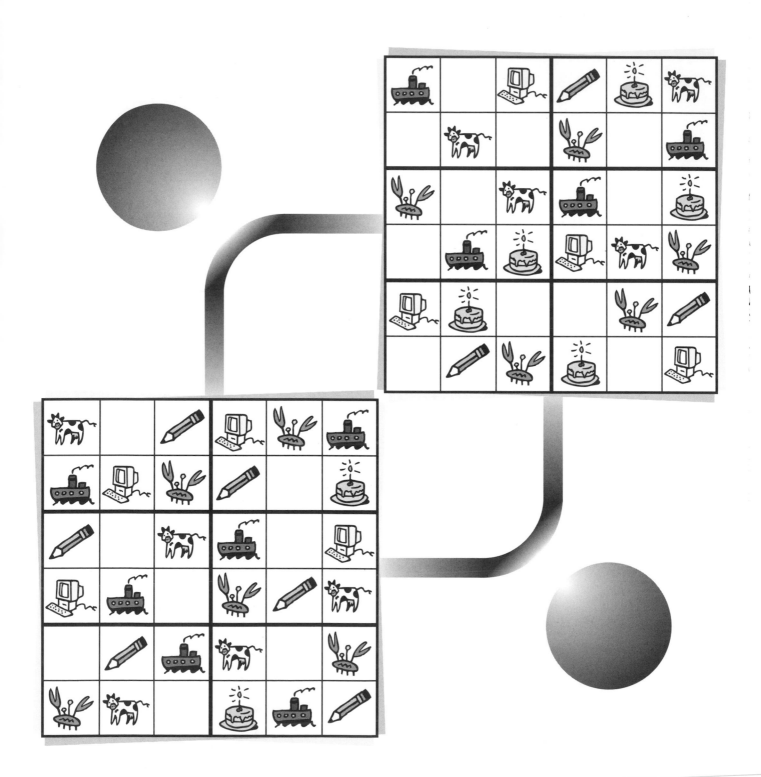

# Snap happy

Draw some of the best things you did last summer in the photographs below.

# Pattern puzzler

This puzzle is a 6 x 6 grid of boxes in which you need to put six sets of patterns. Each pattern must appear once in each row, once in each column, and once in each 3 x 2 box. If any pattern appears twice in the same box, row or column, you have to start all over again!

# Bird word puzzle

Find the words listed below. Words can go horizontally, vertically, and diagonally, and can read forward and backward.

```
I  D  C  J  O  T  W  O  R  R  A  P  S  H  D
S  R  S  E  A  G  U  L  L  M  F  S  W  A  N
E  I  R  K  T  W  C  N  R  H  L  B  R  R  A
A  B  K  E  O  O  I  J  Y  C  A  K  D  E  W
G  G  U  L  H  O  R  J  Z  N  M  R  U  K  X
L  N  G  T  S  S  K  R  K  I  I  O  L  C  Z
E  I  X  W  S  K  I  A  A  F  N  T  O  E  O
P  M  N  M  O  A  W  F  B  P  G  S  D  P  S
E  M  I  C  R  U  S  R  G  U  O  W  G  D  T
L  U  F  O  T  D  O  V  E  N  R  B  E  O  R
I  H  F  V  A  R  S  O  X  G  I  R  M  O  I
C  Y  U  D  B  Y  R  A  N  A  C  K  A  W  C
A  O  P  B  L  P  E  A  C  O  C  K  D  S  H
N  Q  O  A  A  V  U  L  T  U  R  E  H  A  U
I  E  R  U  N  O  C  T  O  U  C  A  N  P  Y
```

| | | | |
|---|---|---|---|
| ALBATROSS | FLAMINGO | PEACOCK | SWAN |
| CANARY | HUMMINGBIRD | PELICAN | TOUCAN |
| CONURE | KINGFISHER | PUFFIN | VULTURE |
| DOVE | KOOKABURRA | SEAGULL | WOODPECKER |
| EAGLE | OSTRICH | SPARROW | |
| FINCH | PARROT | STORK | |

# Crazy clocks

Look carefully at this picture. There are 10 hidden clocks.
Can you find them all?

# Look alikes

Which two spies are identical? Draw a line to match the pair.

# Pick a **picture**

This puzzle is a 6 x 6 grid of boxes in which you need to put six pictures: 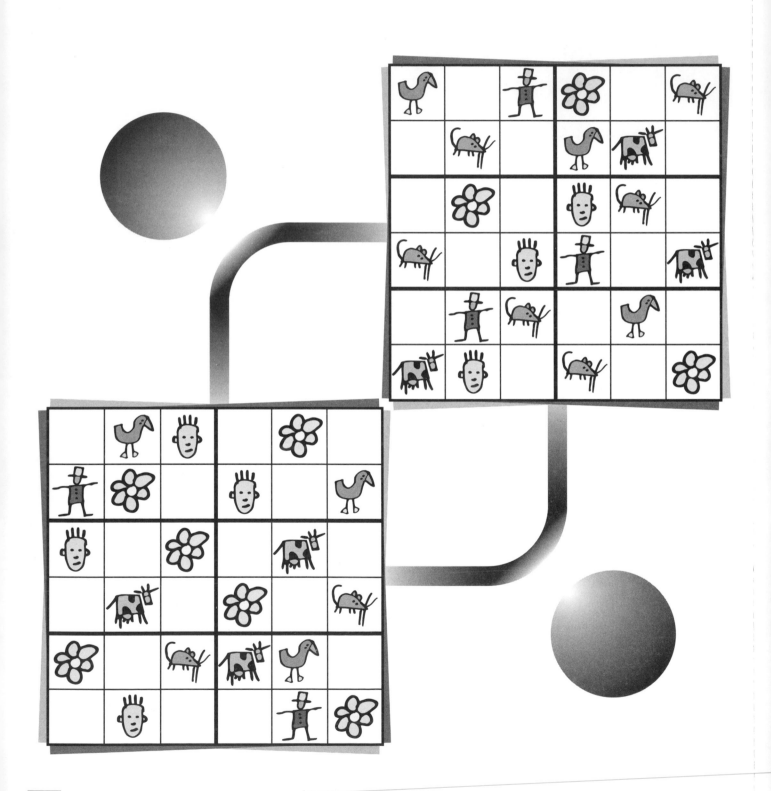. Each picture must appear once in each row, once in each column, and once in each 3 x 2 box. If any picture appears twice in the same box, row or column, you have to start all over again!

# Character word puzzle

Find the words listed below. Words can go horizontally, vertically, and diagonally, and can read forward and backward.

| | | | | | | | | | | | | | | |
|---|---|---|---|---|---|---|---|---|---|---|---|---|---|---|
| H | I | J | O | S | N | O | W | W | H | I | T | E | U | B |
| C | E | F | V | G | N | I | B | M | A | B | I | D | P | C |
| K | Y | R | W | G | A | Z | S | S | Q | L | K | G | M | C |
| J | F | J | B | H | D | O | F | T | M | W | I | L | E | N |
| O | Y | G | U | I | Z | W | O | Q | F | L | G | S | C | I |
| A | J | A | G | M | E | L | V | U | I | V | U | D | I | S |
| D | O | N | A | L | D | D | U | C | K | O | D | N | N | R |
| T | N | N | A | N | C | O | J | M | H | N | A | D | E | E |
| H | O | C | I | Z | C | R | X | Y | J | A | Y | L | E | T |
| N | W | Y | F | D | P | B | E | W | Z | E | F | Y | R | S |
| D | E | K | S | P | D | K | W | R | T | Z | O | E | E | N |
| O | E | O | W | T | C | A | A | R | I | E | O | N | L | O |
| S | A | K | O | I | O | T | L | L | S | V | G | S | L | M |
| X | T | Z | M | Y | L | R | Y | A | Z | F | B | I | A | S |
| C | D | O | V | A | S | M | Y | O | X | T | H | D | K | U |

ALADDIN        DONALD DUCK    MONSTERS INC
BAMBI          GOOFY          SNOW WHITE
CINDERELLA     HERBIE         TARZAN
DISNEYLAND     MICKEY MOUSE   TOY STORY

# Something **fishy!**

Draw the sea creature these fish have just seen swimming towards them.

# Letter sudoku

This puzzle is a 6 x 6 grid of boxes in which you need to put six sets of letters: R, S, K, V, W, P. Each letter must appear once in each row, once in each column, and once in each 3 x 2 box. If any letter appears twice in the same box, row or column, you have to start all over again!

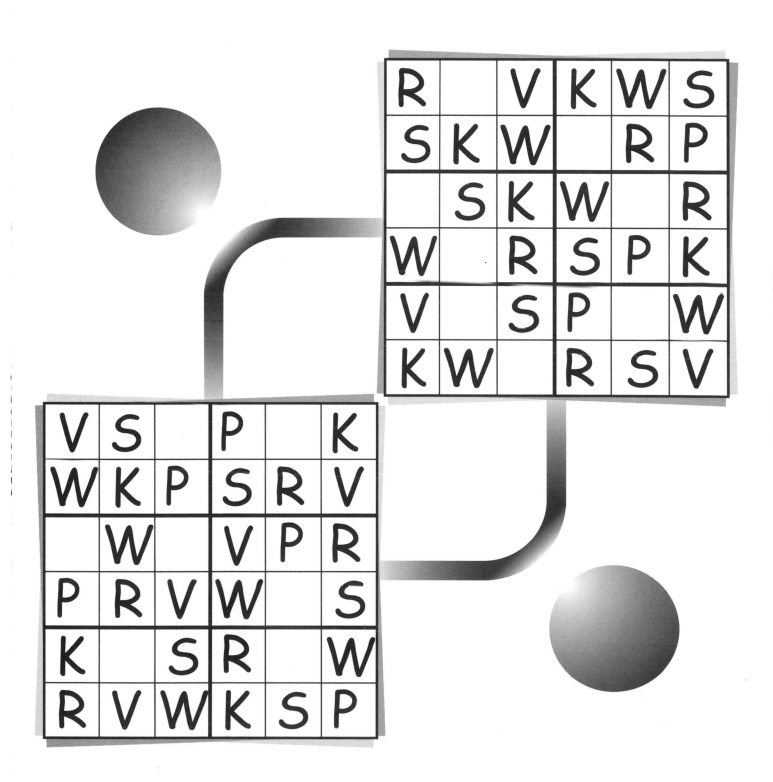

# Missing letters

Fill in the missing letters to complete the names of these spies.

_ A M _ S

L _ U I _ _

M _ R _ A

_ A _ K

# Sudoku

To solve this puzzle, every number from 1 to 9 must appear in each
of the nine vertical columns, in each of the nine horizontal rows,
and in each of the nine boxes.

| | | 8 | 3 | | | | 2 | |
|---|---|---|---|---|---|---|---|---|
| 6 | | | 8 | 2 | 7 | | | |
| | | 2 | | 4 | | 7 | | 6 |
| | 6 | | 9 | | 3 | | 7 | 2 |
| | 4 | 9 | | | | 6 | 3 | |
| 7 | 2 | | 6 | | 4 | | 9 | |
| 1 | | 4 | | 3 | | 9 | | |
| | | | 4 | 6 | 1 | | | 8 |
| | 5 | | | | 8 | 3 | | |

# Dig it!

Archaeologist Phillipa Fogg's done it again! She's discovered something very old and rare. Is it Roman remains, a dinosaur skeleton, or just an old coat hanger? You decide.

# Artist's block

The famous painter, Matt Emulsion, can't think of anything to paint.
Can you paint something for him?

# Shaping up!

This puzzle is a 4 x 4 grid of boxes in which you need to put four sets of shapes: ▲★■●. Each shape must appear once in each row, once in each column, and once in each 2 x 2 box. If any shape appears twice in the same box, row or column, you have to start all over again!

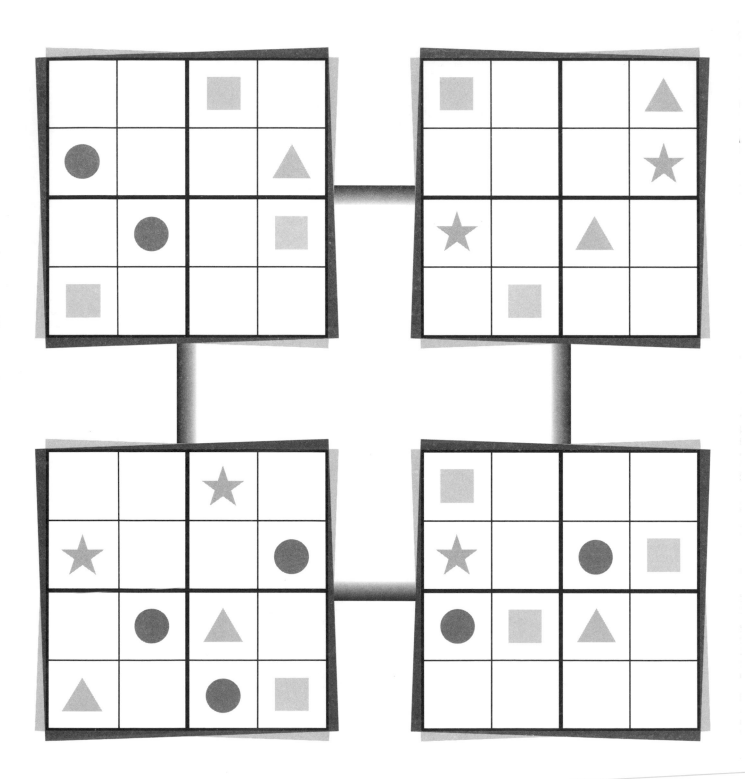

# Don't be late!

Put a mirror along the dotted line to read the letters.
What does the message say? Write it on the lines.

......................................................................

## SPY MEETING AT MIDDAY

_____

_____

# Camping **word puzzle**

Find the words listed below. Words can go horizontally,
vertically, and diagonally, and can read forward and backward.

```
X  G  L  N  E  M  A  H  Q  I  Y  R  F  V  C
E  E  N  B  A  C  K  P  A  C  K  L  H  M  L
D  T  S  O  Y  D  P  V  H  E  A  Y  Q  E  I
A  Q  I  S  S  Y  A  B  A  S  B  R  O  J  W
R  S  E  S  L  G  J  Z  H  H  N  U  G  A  F
M  T  R  V  P  S  N  L  G  A  S  A  R  T  A
Y  O  I  G  Y  M  I  I  V  N  B  E  R  A  C
K  V  F  E  I  G  A  A  S  G  R  B  O  R  I
N  E  P  I  H  M  R  C  N  P  Q  Q  P  P  L
I  O  M  T  T  A  B  I  R  G  Q  Z  E  A  I
F  L  A  S  C  B  P  A  I  P  L  Z  G  U  T
E  V  C  A  S  E  O  Y  U  E  P  N  L  L  I
Z  L  Y  G  E  F  L  A  N  T  E  R  N  I  E
W  Y  D  L  S  M  A  T  C  H  E  S  T  N  S
I  T  S  K  Y  T  E  N  T  D  L  Q  O  A  B
```

| | | |
|---|---|---|
| ARMY KNIFE | FACILITIES | SING SONG |
| BACKPACK | FLASHLIGHT | SLEEPING BAG |
| CAMP FIRE | LANTERN | STOVE |
| CAMPSITE | MATCHES | TARPAULIN |
| CARAVAN | ROPE | TENT |

# Space race

Rock Starjet is approaching a space station but he can't see it.
Draw the space station for him to land on.

# Spells shelves

Wanda the Witch has run out of all the ingredients she needs for her spells. Fill her shelves with the gruesome things she might need.

# Sudoku

To solve this puzzle, every number from 1 to 9 must appear in each
of the nine vertical columns, in each of the nine horizontal rows,
and in each of the nine boxes.

| 4 |   |   | 5 |   | 1 |   | 3 | 7 |
|---|---|---|---|---|---|---|---|---|
| 3 |   |   | 4 | 6 |   | 5 |   |   |
|   | 5 | 6 |   |   |   | 9 |   |   |
| 2 |   |   |   | 4 |   |   | 9 | 8 |
|   | 6 |   | 1 |   | 3 |   | 7 |   |
| 8 | 1 |   |   | 7 |   |   |   | 6 |
|   |   | 5 |   |   |   | 8 | 2 |   |
|   |   | 7 |   | 5 | 2 |   |   | 9 |
| 1 | 2 |   | 9 |   | 4 |   |   | 5 |

# Library spy

Susan the spy is researching a new case at the library.
Can you find the differences between these two pictures?

# Pattern sudoku

This puzzle is a 6 x 6 grid of boxes in which you need to put six sets of patterns. Each pattern must appear once in each row, once in each column, and once in each 3 x 2 box. If any pattern appears twice in the same box, row or column, you have to start all over again!

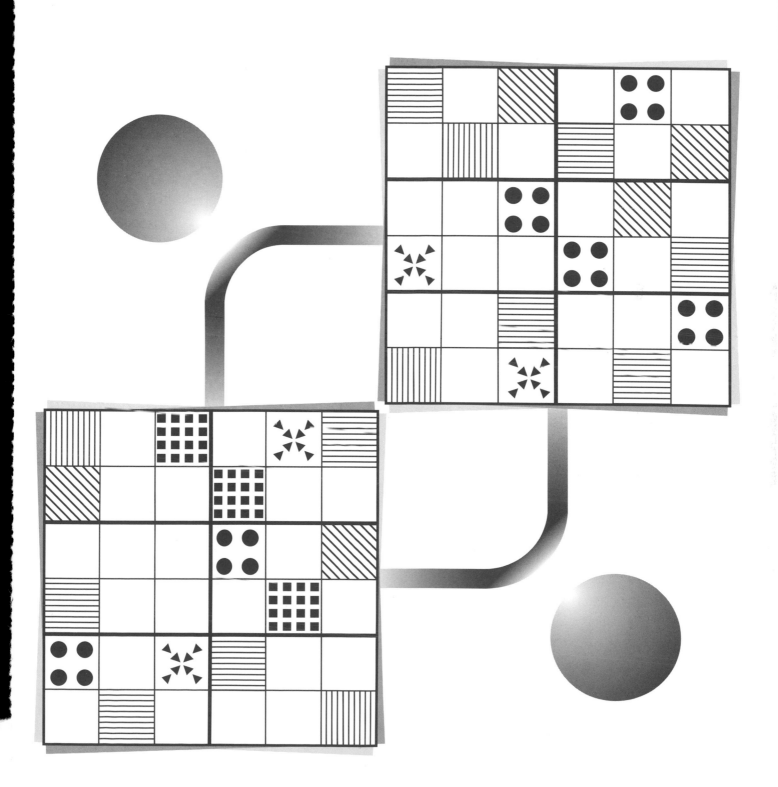

# A day's work

This salesman has just paid a visit to Castle Dracula.
He won't be making that mistake again! Draw the castle
and make it look really scary!

Castle
Dracula

# Number rumba

This puzzle is a 6 x 6 grid of boxes in which you need to put six sets of numbers: 1,2,3,4,5,6. Each number must appear once in each row, once in each column, and once in each 3 x 2 box. If any number appears twice in the same box, row or column, you have to start all over again!

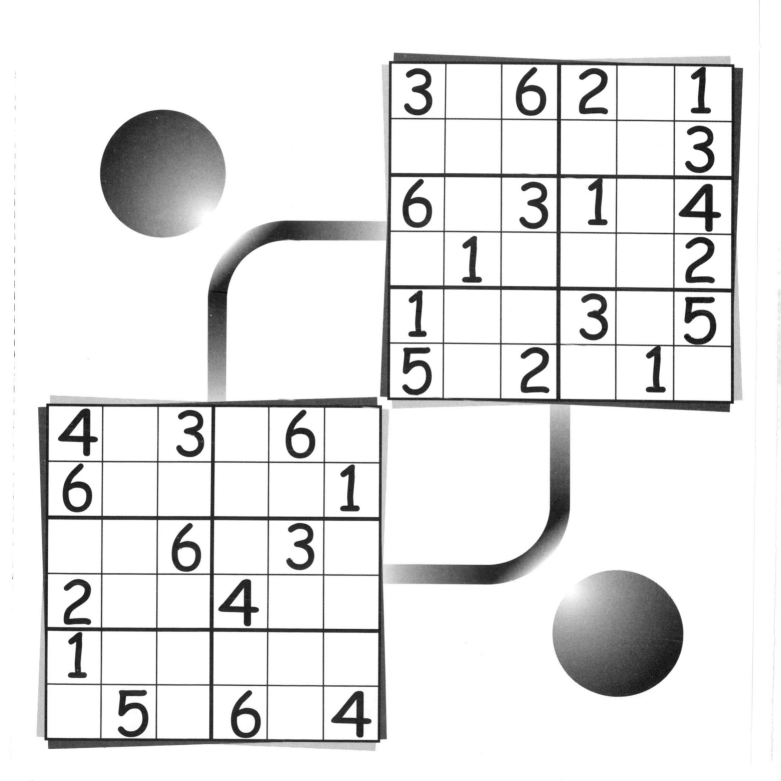

# Nightmare!

This man has had a nightmare about a monster.
Draw what you think the monster looked like.

# Shopping word puzzle

The pictures are clues. Look for these words in the grid.
You will find them by reading across or down.
Circle the words as you find them.

| N | M | F | H | I | R | Y | O | Y |
|---|---|---|---|---|---|---|---|---|
| D | E | S | H | A | M | P | O | O |
| R | E | N | L | P | W | Q | C | G |
| F | S | O | A | P | K | L | D | H |
| B | G | U | R | L | P | C | Z | U |
| U | S | F | B | E | H | H | M | R |
| T | R | I | Y | S | U | E | C | T |
| T | L | S | O | W | Q | E | R | E |
| E | J | H | Q | I | U | S | F | E |
| R | K | F | D | B | R | E | A | D |

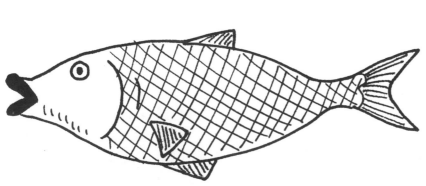

# Letter sudoku

This puzzle is a 6 x 6 grid of boxes in which you need to put six sets of letters: D, E, J, H, O, B. Each letter must appear once in each row, once in each column, and once in each 3 x 2 box. If any letter appears twice in the same box, row or column, you have to start all over again!

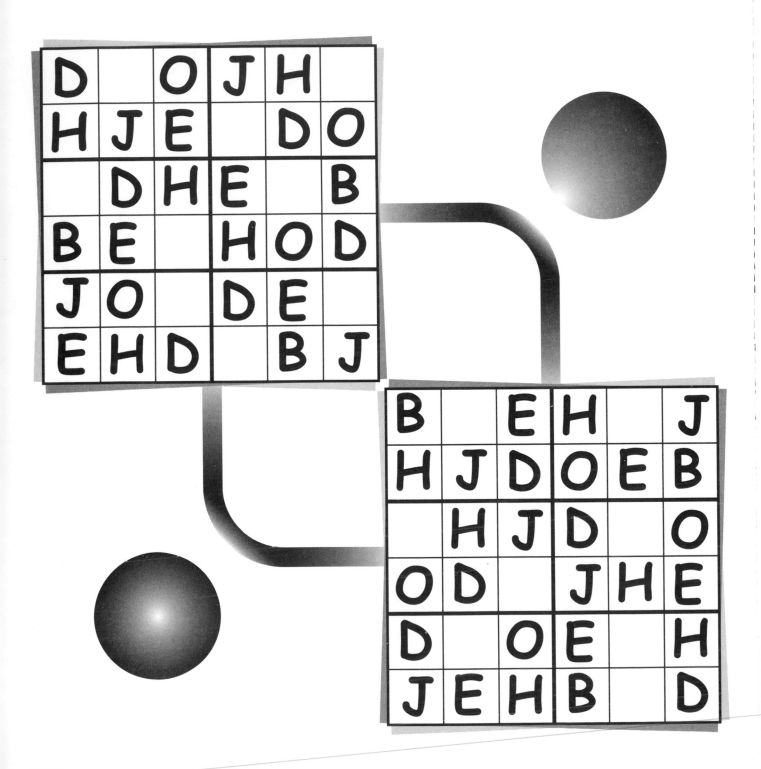

# Sudoku

To solve this puzzle, every number from 1 to 9 must appear in each of the nine vertical columns, in each of the nine horizontal rows, and in each of the nine boxes.

| 6 | 3 |   |   |   |   | 4 |   | 7 |
|---|---|---|---|---|---|---|---|---|
|   |   |   | 3 | 7 |   | 9 |   | 6 |
| 4 | 5 |   | 9 |   | 1 |   |   |   |
|   |   | 5 | 1 |   | 2 | 7 | 3 |   |
|   | 4 |   |   |   |   |   | 2 |   |
|   | 2 | 3 | 7 |   | 8 | 6 |   |   |
|   |   |   | 2 |   | 7 |   | 4 | 3 |
| 3 |   | 1 |   | 8 | 9 |   |   |   |
| 2 |   | 4 |   |   |   |   | 7 | 9 |

# Airport word puzzle

Find the words listed below. Words can go horizontally, vertically, and diagonally, and can read forward and backward.

| | | | | | | | | | | | | | | |
|---|---|---|---|---|---|---|---|---|---|---|---|---|---|---|
| V | K | C | O | S | D | N | I | W | F | S | Y | J | S | X |
| P | I | N | D | P | T | Z | S | L | H | A | T | S | Y | D |
| I | Y | E | E | F | H | R | I | U | W | M | A | O | E | R |
| L | R | H | W | S | W | G | O | N | I | P | F | P | W | K |
| O | O | O | B | I | H | E | U | P | G | T | A | D | P | N |
| T | R | L | V | T | N | R | D | N | S | R | C | A | E | S |
| P | E | I | O | S | R | G | I | U | T | S | I | A | M | A |
| E | G | D | N | X | L | D | G | U | T | R | A | O | S | R |
| G | N | A | V | I | R | A | R | A | L | Y | T | P | W | E |
| A | E | Y | A | A | K | E | N | I | L | S | F | H | J | H |
| G | S | F | O | N | G | C | N | I | U | L | Q | R | U | L |
| G | S | B | U | A | J | E | E | C | M | Q | E | K | E | P |
| U | A | Z | T | H | C | Q | B | H | P | R | G | R | N | E |
| L | P | E | A | W | U | U | N | L | C | J | E | I | Y | Z |
| S | S | E | D | R | A | W | E | T | S | J | A | T | A | Y |

AIRLINE
BOARDING PASS
CHECK IN
CUSTOMS
DEPARTURE GATE
DUTY FREE

FLIGHT
HOLIDAY
LUGGAGE
PASSENGER
PASSPORT
PILOT

RUNWAY
STEWARDESS
SUITCASE
TERMINAL
VIEWING GALLERY
WINDSOCK

# Disguise this guy

Can you disguise this secret agent so that no one will see him?
Copy the pictures in the panel to make your disguise.

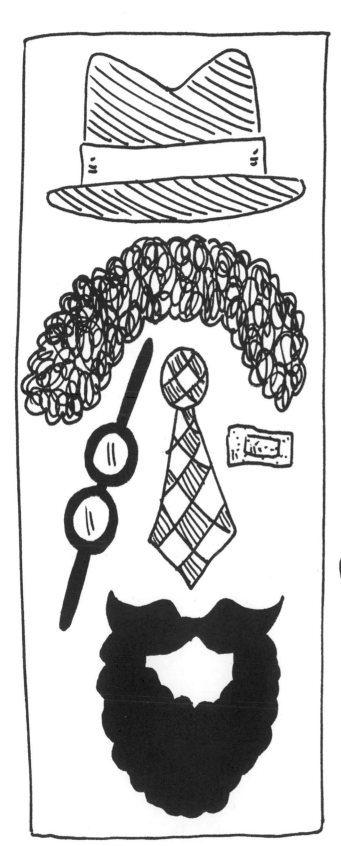

# Letter sudoku

This puzzle is a 4 x 4 grid of boxes in which you need to put four sets of letters: T, Q, Z, N. Each letter must appear once in each row, once in each column, and once in each 2 x 2 box. If any letter appears twice in the same box, row or column, you have to start all over again!

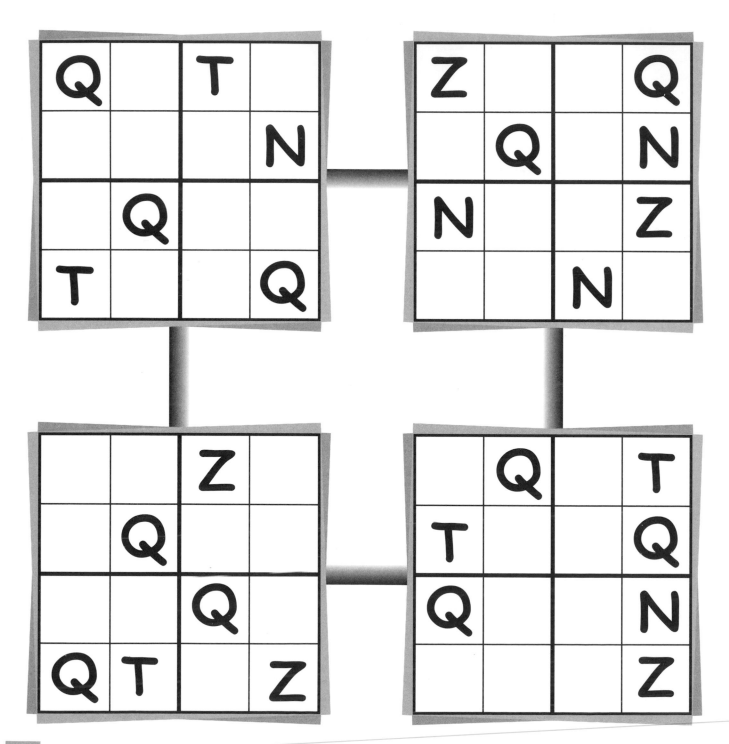

# Dreamer

What do you like to dream about? Draw it in the cloud.

# Awesome anagrams

Can you unscramble the letters to discover the secret words?
The pictures are clues.

phamitosoppu

lionbursac

rizwad

hepetolne

# You are **a star!**

# ANSWERS

**4. Countries word puzzle**

| C | A | N | A | D | A | R | T | | E |
|---|---|---|---|---|---|---|---|---|---|
| H | Z | W | M | L | D | C | O | | N |
| I | N | D | I | A | R | H | I | | G |
| N | K | A | S | O | A | I | P | | L |
| A | H | S | R | X | M | L | I | | A |
| C | V | Y | A | N | K | E | D | | N |
| G | R | E | E | C | E | S | | | D |
| P | E | K | L | J | T | L | F | | I |
| D | C | S | E | Q | U | H | P | | M |
| H | O | L | L | A | N | D | R | | U |

**5. Hidden word**
EGYPT

**7. Whispers**
meet by the see-saw

**8. Secret fashions**

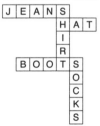

| a | x | k | a | w | l | o | d | e | t |
|---|---|---|---|---|---|---|---|---|---|
| g | r | y | n | m | b | a | v | z | w |
| h | a | t | b | g | d | l | j | y | s |
| r | w | a | a | l | p | r | s | l | p |
| e | f | s | a | o | m | u | k | i | k |
| d | j | k | e | v | s | a | i | x | c |
| e | g | m | q | e | t | h | r | k | p |
| d | r | e | s | s | u | i | t | f | w |
| p | h | u | q | s | d | t | y | o | p |

**9. Crossword in code**

```
J E A N S
      H A T
      I
      R
B O O T S
      O
      C
      K
      S
```

**10. Coded sports**
TENNIS  HOCKEY  SKIING  SKATING

**11. Question time**
a) 12

**12. Puzzles for 4**

| 12 | + | 4 | = | 16 |
|---|---|---|---|---|
| − | | + | | − |
| 10 | − | 2 | = | 8 |
| = | | = | | = |
| 2 | + | 6 | = | 8 |

| 5 | + | 11 | = | 16 |
|---|---|---|---|---|
| + | | + | | + |
| 6 | + | 3 | = | 9 |
| = | | = | | = |
| 11 | + | 14 | = | 25 |

| 4 | + | 9 | = | 13 |
|---|---|---|---|---|
| + | | − | | + |
| 10 | − | 3 | = | 7 |
| = | | = | | = |
| 14 | + | 6 | = | 20 |

| 3 | × | 4 | = | 12 |
|---|---|---|---|---|
| × | | × | | × |
| 3 | × | 2 | = | 6 |
| = | | = | | = |
| 9 | × | 8 | = | 72 |

**16. Word trail**

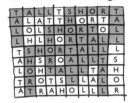

| ¹E | L | E | P | H | A | N | ²T | O |
|---|---|---|---|---|---|---|---|---|
| L | | | | | | | P | |
| G | | | 3 | | 4 | | A | |
| ¹⁰A | | | | | | | R | |
| E | | | | | | | R | |
| R | | | | | | | O | |
| ⁹T | | | | | | | T | |
| I | | 7 | | | 8 | | R | |
| B | | | | | | | A | |
| B | | | | | | | I | |
| ⁸A | | | | | | | N | |
| R | | | | | | | A | |
| E | H | T | A | E | F | A | E | L⁶ |

**20. Different-sized dragons**

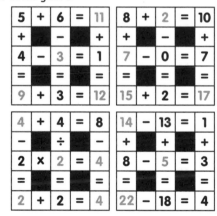

| T | A | L | L | T | S | H | O | R | T |
|---|---|---|---|---|---|---|---|---|---|
| A | L | A | T | T | H | O | R | T | A |
| L | O | L | S | H | O | R | T | O | L |
| L | H | L | H | O | R | T | A | L | L |
| T | S | H | O | R | T | A | L | L | L |
| A | H | S | R | O | A | L | L | T | S |
| L | O | H | T | A | L | L | T | A | H |
| T | R | O | T | S | L | L | A | L | O |
| A | T | R | A | H | O | L | L | L | R |

**22. Grids galore**

| 5 | + | 6 | = | 11 |
|---|---|---|---|---|
| + | | − | | + |
| 4 | − | 3 | = | 1 |
| = | | = | | = |
| 9 | + | 3 | = | 12 |

| 8 | + | 2 | = | 10 |
|---|---|---|---|---|
| + | | − | | + |
| 7 | − | 0 | = | 7 |
| = | | = | | = |
| 15 | + | 2 | = | 17 |

| 4 | + | 4 | = | 8 |
|---|---|---|---|---|
| − | | ÷ | | − |
| 2 | × | 2 | = | 4 |
| = | | = | | = |
| 2 | + | 2 | = | 4 |

| 14 | − | 13 | = | 1 |
|---|---|---|---|---|
| + | | + | | + |
| 8 | − | 5 | = | 3 |
| = | | = | | = |
| 22 | − | 18 | = | 4 |

**23. Witch shadow?**
C

**26. Mysterious message**
TAKE THE PATH TO THE WOOD AND I WILL MEET
YOU AT THE LOGS IN THE MIDDLE AT TEN

**29. Quiz time**
b) its tongue

**30. Pointing puzzle**

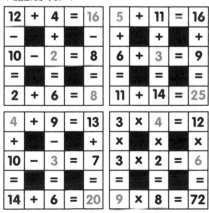

| D | S | P | O | T | K | I | N | G | I |
|---|---|---|---|---|---|---|---|---|---|
| S | W | O | R | D | N | F | E | R | N |
| G | B | I | A | G | A | O | A | F | R |
| C | T | D | R | A | G | O | N | V | A |
| B | O | E | M | N | H | T | A | I | L |
| H | E | L | M | E | T | F | I | N | F |
| I | D | R | A | E | F | U | R | N | Y |

**31.** Size wise

SMALL  BIG  HUGE
LITTLE  TINY  GIANT
MASSIVE  SHORT
TALL  GREAT

**32.** Jungle numbers

| 3 | + | 9 | = | 12 |
|---|---|---|---|---|
| × |  | × |  | ÷ |
| 12 | ÷ | 2 | = | 6 |
| = |  | = |  | = |
| 36 | ÷ | 18 | = | 2 |

| 2 | × | 6 | = | 12 |
|---|---|---|---|---|
| + |  | − |  | − |
| 3 | − | 1 | = | 2 |
| = |  | = |  | = |
| 5 | + | 5 | = | 10 |

| 15 | ÷ | 3 | = | 5 |
|---|---|---|---|---|
| − |  | × |  | + |
| 3 | − | 2 | = | 1 |
| = |  | = |  | = |
| 12 | − | 6 | = | 6 |

| 19 | − | 16 | = | 3 |
|---|---|---|---|---|
| + |  | − |  | + |
| 2 | + | 12 | = | 14 |
| = |  | = |  | = |
| 21 | − | 4 | = | 17 |

**36.** What's gone wrong?

STARS AND SUN
GIRAFFE IN PARK
FRAME OF SWING
BOY WITH SAUCEPAN ON HEAD

**37.** Questions and answers

1 TREE
2 STING
3 STY
4 OARS
5 EGGS

**40.** Helicopter numbers

| S | E | V | E | N |  |  |
|---|---|---|---|---|---|---|
| I |  |  |  | O | N | E |
| X |  |  |  | U |  | L |
| T | W | O |  | G |  | E |
| E |  |  |  | H |  | V |
| E | I | G | H | T |  | E |
| N |  |  |  |  |  | N |

**41.** Quiz time
a) graphite

**42.** Crossed swords and words

(crossword: SWORD / DRAGON / KNIGHT / FIGHT / HELMET)

Who do you think will win this sword fight between the dragon with the helmet and the knight?

**45.** Walter's shopping list
SOCKS  BATS  JARS  WAND  LIZARD

**46.** Crack the code
WE ARE GOING TO THE CIRCUS TONIGHT.
MY FAMILY IS GOING ON A PLANE TOMORROW.
THE WEATHER IS VERY COLD TODAY.

**47.** Code continued!
WOULD YOU LIKE SOME CHOCOLATE CAKE?
MEET ME AT THE ICE RINK THIS AFTERNOON.
WE WILL WIN THE CUP THIS SEASON!

**48.** Busy number bees

| 7 | − | 6 | = | 1 |
|---|---|---|---|---|
| + |  | − |  | + |
| 1 | + | 2 | = | 3 |
| = |  | = |  | = |
| 8 | − | 4 | = | 4 |

| 7 | + | 4 | = | 11 |
|---|---|---|---|---|
| × |  | − |  | + |
| 3 | × | 3 | = | 9 |
| = |  | = |  | = |
| 21 | − | 1 | = | 20 |

| 12 | + | 3 | = | 15 |
|---|---|---|---|---|
| − |  | × |  | ÷ |
| 6 | − | 1 | = | 5 |
| = |  | = |  | = |
| 6 | − | 3 | = | 3 |

| 4 | + | 9 | = | 13 |
|---|---|---|---|---|
| + |  | + |  | + |
| 10 | − | 3 | = | 7 |
| = |  | = |  | = |
| 14 | + | 6 | = | 20 |

**49.** Quiz time
c) turkey

**51.** Which way?

CHINA    NORWAY
CANADA   BRAZIL
IRELAND  EGYPT

**52.** Animal spies

rabbit   owl
mouse    fox

**53/54.** Four seasons
DAFFODILS APPEAR
SUNSHINE TIME
LEAVES FALL FROM TREES
WE BUILD A SNOWMAN

**55.** Knights alike
3 4 8

**56.** Blowing bubbles

| 12 | + | 4 | = | 16 |
|---|---|---|---|---|
| − |  | + |  | − |
| 10 | − | 2 | = | 8 |
| = |  | = |  | = |
| 2 | + | 6 | = | 8 |

| 2 | + | 8 | = | 10 |
|---|---|---|---|---|
| − |  | − |  | − |
| 1 | + | 2 | = | 3 |
| = |  | = |  | = |
| 1 | + | 6 | = | 7 |

| 5 | + | 11 | = | 16 |
|---|---|---|---|---|
| + |  | + |  | + |
| 6 | + | 3 | = | 9 |
| = |  | = |  | = |
| 11 | + | 14 | = | 25 |

| 3 | + | 6 | = | 9 |
|---|---|---|---|---|
| + |  | − |  | − |
| 2 | + | 4 | = | 6 |
| = |  | = |  | = |
| 5 | − | 2 | = | 3 |

**57.** Mirror mysteries
WRITE YOUR NAME HERE

459

**62.** Quiz time
c) butterfly

**63.** Quiz time
d) e

**65.** Hidden word
JULIA

**66.** What's the difference?
1 BOW TIE
2 DIFFERENT EARS
3 SMOKE RING
4 HORNS ON SNOUT
5 DRAGON'S FINGERS
6 EXTRA TOOTH
7 FEATHER ON HELMET
8 EXTRA STRAW
9 STRAW BENDING DIFFERENT WAY
10 DRAGON WEARING WATCH
11 SPINE ON DRAGON'S HEAD
12 FLAMES
13 CIRCLES ON HELMET
14 DIFFERENT WORD

**68.** Messy work

```
      E
    F I V E
      G
      H   T
  F O U R T E E N
  O       N
  R
  T W O
  Y
```

**69.** Quiz time
b) hands

**70.** Wizard word puzzle

**71.** Spell book
1 BIRD ON PERCH
2 BIRD'S FEEDING CUP MISSING
3 MOON MISSING FROM WIZARD'S HAT
4 LID FROM INK POT MISSING
5 LIZARD'S FANG MISSING
6 STAR ON LEG MISSING
7 STRIPE ON SOCK MISSING
8 BUBBLE FROM CAULDRON MISSING

**72/73.** Global codes
HOLLAND
FRANCE
ITALY
SPAIN
AUSTRALIA
AMERICA

**76.** Underwater problems

| 6 | − | 1 | = | 5 |
|---|---|---|---|---|
| + |   | × |   | + |
| 2 | × | 1 | = | 2 |
| = |   | = |   | = |
| 8 | − | 1 | = | 7 |

| 3 | × | 2 | = | 6 |
|---|---|---|---|---|
| + |   | − |   | − |
| 1 | × | 1 | = | 1 |
| = |   | = |   | = |
| 4 | + | 1 | = | 5 |

| 5 | − | 3 | = | 2 |
|---|---|---|---|---|
| + |   | ÷ |   | + |
| 2 | × | 3 | = | 6 |
| = |   | = |   | = |
| 7 | + | 1 | = | 8 |

| 4 | + | 2 | = | 6 |
|---|---|---|---|---|
| × |   | − |   | + |
| 2 | + | 1 | = | 3 |
| = |   | = |   | = |
| 8 | + | 1 | = | 9 |

**77.** Quiz time
a) a doe

**80.** Morse code
SOS-the code to signal for help

**81.** Number creatures

| 4 | × | 4 | = | 16 |
|---|---|---|---|----|
| ÷ |   | ÷ |   | ÷ |
| 2 | × | 4 | = | 8 |
| = |   | = |   | = |
| 2 | × | 1 | = | 2 |

| 4 | + | 12 | = | 16 |
|---|---|----|---|----|
| + |   | + |   | − |
| 14 | − | 2 | = | 12 |
| = |   | = |   | = |
| 18 | − | 14 | = | 4 |

| 6 | + | 2 | = | 8 |
|---|---|---|---|---|
| ÷ |   | + |   | + |
| 2 | − | 1 | = | 1 |
| = |   | = |   | = |
| 3 | × | 3 | = | 9 |

| 4 | + | 5 | = | 9 |
|---|---|---|---|---|
| × |   | + |   | × |
| 3 | − | 1 | = | 2 |
| = |   | = |   | = |
| 12 | + | 6 | = | 18 |

**83.** Creepy crossword

```
C A S T L E
    O
    M U M M Y
    B       C
    W I T C H O
    G     G   B
D R A G O N S P I D E R
      E O   T   B
        S       
        T       
```
CASTLE, TOMB, MUMMY, WITCH, GHOST, COBWEB, DRAGON, SPIDER

**86.** Quiz time
a) a hummingbird

**87.** Semaphore
HAVE YOU ANY FOOD?

**91.** Seeing stars
Hat F has the fewest stars.

**92.** Shipwrecked numbers

**93.** Spies like us!
Which spy is the odd one?
Spy D

**94.** Wheel of mystery
MEET ME AT THE FAIRGROUND AT 2 O'CLOCK

**95.** Word trail

```
T O M A T O C T O
A               P
E   [1]   [2]   U
S               S
E   [3]   [4]   T
S               R
S               A
A   [5]   [6]   W
L               B
G   [7]   [8]   E
O               R
R         [9]   R
F               Y
A E L I A T H C A
```

**98.** Quiz time
c) 4

**99.** Puzzle wheel
LOUISE
POPLAR

**100/101.** Hide-and-seek
9 bats
7 ghosts
4 skulls

**102.** Monkey problems

```
N I N E     S
I     I     I
N     G     X
E I G H T   T
T     T     E
E           E
E I G H T E E N
N
```

**103.** Quiz time
a) a crater

**105.** Ancient symbols
many buffalo in valley
many fish in water
feast tonight

**106.** Wizard challenge!
4

**107.** Who's-who crossword

```
            W
    W I N N I E
W A N D A   L
      R     L
    W E N D Y   I
    A       O   A
    L       L   M
    T       P
    E       H
    R
```

**112/113.** What's the time, Wardolph?
WARDOLPH WAKING UP 8:00AM
WARDOLPH EATING BREAKFAST 8:30AM
WARDOLPH LEAVING HIS HOUSE 10:00AM
WARDOLPH GETTING ON A MAGIC CARPET 10:20AM
WARDOLPH OUTSIDE WANDA'S WANDS 12:30PM
WARDOLPH LEAVING WANDA'S WANDS 1:15PM
WARDOLPH AT HOME HAVING A DRINK 6:30PM
WARDOLPH ASLEEP WITH HIS NEW WAND 9:00PM

**114.** Liftoff!

| 9 | × | 2 | = | 18 | 5 | + | 6 | = | 11 |
|---|---|---|---|----|---|---|---|---|----|
| − | | − | | ÷ | + | | − | | + |
| 3 | ÷ | 1 | = | 3 | 7 | − | 4 | = | 3 |
| = | | = | | = | = | | = | | = |
| 6 | × | 1 | = | 6 | 12 | + | 2 | = | 14 |
| 10 | × | 2 | = | 20 | 2 | + | 2 | = | 4 |
| ÷ | | + | | ÷ | + | | − | | + |
| 5 | − | 1 | = | 4 | 9 | − | 2 | = | 7 |
| = | | = | | = | = | | = | | = |
| 2 | + | 3 | = | 5 | 11 | + | 0 | = | 11 |

**115.** Quiz time
d) 8

**116.** Jumble grumble
iceberg
hedgehog
chimney
toadstool

**117.** Quiz time
b) China

**121.** Secret agent's message
See you at the pool later

**124.** Ski numbers

```
S I X T Y S I X A
E B Z C U D P R E
V Q S F X V G T A
E L E V E N B H D
N H V C I F H I G
T J E K W I L R O
Y P N J Q T M T F
O X Q F O U R Y I
N V R L S K U P V
E I G H T Y O N E
```

**125.** Spooky wood word puzzle

```
B A T R S C V Y O
S R A T Z M L D P
P N F O Q C R O W
I H A W D B X G B
D J A L X F F A E
E L I Z A R D I E
R H F D Y O D F S
C A T I B G W H Z
S D G R H X O J X
B U T T E R F L Y
```

**127. Crossword puzzle**

```
            B   F
            E   A
  A S T R O N A U T
    H       R
    A       D
  S U M M E R
    P
    O
  S O A P
```

**129. Fishy tale**
THE ONE IN THE MIDDLE

**130. Puzzle wheel**
SALMON
BRAZIL

**131. Quiz time**
b) by squirting ink

**136. World trail**

```
D O L P H I N E T
A               E
O               L
R               E
H               P
C               H
A               O
E               N
T               E
S           G   G
E           O   O
N           A   A
O I S I V E L E T
```

**137. Where in the world?**

```
M E X I C O X S J
A D F L M B I O A
L Z I T A L Y X P
A G Y V G H A N A
Y J F P K A I W N
S H T C R Z Q I Q
I R E L A N D U P
A R D K M X H G E
J K C T U P U I R
T U R K E Y E M U
```

**138. Batty problems**

```
        F I F T Y T W O
  T E N     W       N
    L     S E V E N E
    E     I     L
    V     X     V
    E     T H R E E
    N I N E
          E
          N
```

**139. Eye-spy**
13 pairs of eyes

**143. It's a jumble**
telephone
rocking chair
candle
squirrel

**146. Literary numbers**

```
            T
  F O U R T W O
  I         E
  S E V E N T E E N
  E     W   T
    F O R T Y
        H
        R
        E
      T W E N T Y
```

**149. Secret invitation**
Will you come to my party?

**150. Woodland wonder!**
read this secret
meet me at the park

**151. Where be the treasure?**
treasure hidden under trees on witch island

**156. Quiz time**
a) tongue

**157. Number crunchers**

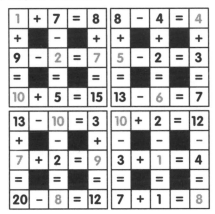

```
1  + 7  = 8      8  - 4 = 4
+    -    +      +    +   +
9  - 2  = 7      5  - 2 = 3
=         =      =        =
10 + 5  = 15     13 - 6 = 7

13 - 10 = 3      10 + 2 = 12
+    -           -    -    -
7  + 2  = 9      3  + 1 = 4
=         =      =    =    =
20 - 8  = 12     7  + 1 = 8
```

**158. Which hat?**
a-2
b-4
c-1
d-3

**159. Dragon differences**
1 STAR MISSING
2 SMOKE
3 MOUNTAIN MISSING
4 BAT'S FEET MISSING
5 SCALES MISSING
6 TOE MISSING
7. WING MISSING
8. SPIKE ON HEAD MISSING

**160. Jigsaw puzzle**
a-e
b-h
c-g
d-f

**161. What's gone wrong?**
CROCODILE IN RIVER
FLYING SHEEP
MONSTER BEHIND MOUNTAIN
SHIP ON MOUNTAIN
TEAPOT ON BOY'S HEAD

**164.** Puzzle wheel
GRAPES
ORANGE

**165.** Quiz time
b) 32

**168.** A giant step

**169.** Questions and answers
1 light
2 rainbow
3 horse
4 rice
5 space shuttle

**170.** Hidden word
OAK

**171.** Word trail

```
H A M M E R  R A F T  T
S        I         R
I        F         A
F R      U         I
U        S         N
S        E         E
E        V         W
V        O         S
O        L         P
L        G O       A
G                  P
O   D N O P M A L I A/E/R
```

**172.** Quiz time
a) feathers

**173.** Clever crossword
```
                19 − 16 =
                    T
       29 − 12 =    H
           S        R
8 + 4 =  T W E L V E
           V  4 x 5 = E
25 ÷ 5 = F I V E
           N        T
30 − 15 = F I F T E E N
           E        N
           E        T
           N        Y
```

**176.** Jumble scramble
water lily
tractor
seaweed
saxophone

**177.** Quiz time
b) Egypt

**181.** Quiz time
b) an ostrich

**184.** Desert puzzle
```
T F O U R T E E N N
H O Q W E T Y U I I
I R I O P A S D N N
R T W E N T Y X E E
T Y F G H J K L T T
Y T Z N F I F T Y Y
N W C I V B M Q N N
I O W N E R T Y I I
N U I E S E V E N N
E A D G J D S B E E
```

**185.** Quiz time
b) a giant tortoise

**187.** Potions
heaviest - 2kg of tentacles
lightest - 10kg of frogspawn

**188.** Quiz time
c) bees

**193.** Quiz time
c) every 4 years

**194.** Puzzle cobweb
CAULDRON

**195.** Molehill madness

| 2 | + | 10 | = | 12 | | 12 | + | 2 | = | 14 |
|---|---|----|---|----|---|----|---|---|---|----|
| + | | − | | + | | − | | + | | − |
| 7 | − | 3 | = | 4 | | 8 | − | 2 | = | 6 |
| = | | = | | = | | = | | = | | = |
| 9 | + | 7 | = | 16 | | 4 | + | 4 | = | 8 |

| 4 | + | 8 | = | 12 | | 10 | + | 6 | = | 16 |
|---|---|----|---|----|---|----|---|---|---|----|
| + | | − | | + | | − | | + | | − |
| 10 | − | 2 | = | 8 | | 5 | − | 4 | = | 1 |
| = | | = | | = | | = | | = | | = |
| 14 | + | 6 | = | 20 | | 5 | + | 10 | = | 15 |

**198.** Crossword puzzle

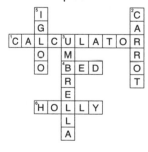

```
   5I              2C
    G               A
 1C A L C 3U L A T O R
    O     M         R
    O    4B E D     O
          R         T
          E
         6H O L L Y
          L
          A
```

**199.** Quiz time
b) blue whale

**202.** What's gone wrong?
MOUSE FLYING
CHIMNEY IN TREES
DEER WEARING HAT
PENCIL TRUNK
MOLE WEARING GLASSES

**203.** A fairy flit

**206.** Quiz time
b) a limbo

**207.** Questions and answers
1 attic
2 tomorrow
3 butter
4 stallion
5 cook

**208.** Word wizard
FEATHERS

**209.** Formula 1 numbers

**212.** Word trail

**214.** Quiz time
a) in its pouch

**215.** Questions and answers
1 dog
2 stars
3 nanny
4 top
5 wine

**217.** Number squares

| 10 | + | 2 | = | 12 | | 9 | − | 3 | = | 6 |
|---|---|---|---|---|---|---|---|---|---|---|
| + | | | | + | | + | | − | | + |
| 7 | − | 2 | = | 5 | | 2 | + | 2 | = | 4 |
| = | | | | = | | = | | = | | = |
| 17 | − | 0 | = | 17 | | 11 | − | 1 | = | 10 |

| 15 | − | 7 | = | 8 | | 7 | + | 3 | = | 10 |
|---|---|---|---|---|---|---|---|---|---|---|
| − | | | | − | | + | | − | | + |
| 5 | − | 3 | = | 2 | | 7 | − | 2 | = | 5 |
| = | | | | = | | = | | = | | = |
| 10 | − | 4 | = | 6 | | 14 | + | 1 | = | 15 |

**221.** Coded letter
HELP! NEED TO CAST A SPELL.

**222.** Quiz time
d) to tell other wolves where they are

**223.** Animal magic

| 12 | + | 12 | = | 24 | | 2 | × | 3 | = | 6 |
|---|---|---|---|---|---|---|---|---|---|---|
| − | | | | − | | × | | × | | × |
| 6 | + | 8 | = | 14 | | 6 | × | 1 | = | 6 |
| = | | | | = | | = | | = | | = |
| 6 | + | 4 | = | 10 | | 12 | × | 3 | = | 36 |

| 2 | + | 7 | = | 9 | | 10 | − | 5 | = | 5 |
|---|---|---|---|---|---|---|---|---|---|---|
| + | | | | − | | − | | + | | − |
| 2 | + | 5 | = | 7 | | 2 | + | 3 | = | 5 |
| = | | | | = | | = | | = | | = |
| 4 | − | 2 | = | 2 | | 8 | − | 8 | = | 0 |

**225.** Word puzzle

**226.** Robo search

## 227. Starting grid

```
      B
S M A S H
      T
      T
      E
M I C R O C H I P
      Y   O
          N
T R A N S M I T
          R
      P O W E R
          L
```

## 228. Crossword puzzle

```
        ⁴A
        L
    ¹B  A
²F L O W E R S
    N   M
    E
   ⁵S T A R ³S
        I
        S
        T
        E
        R
```

## 229. Secret postcards
AMERICA
RUSSIA
KENYA

## 231. Find the robots

## 232. Quiz time
c) sting

## 233. Kitten numbers

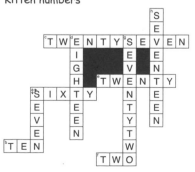

## 234. Word magic
BROOM, STICK, SICK, TICK, ROOM, BOOM, TRICK,
IT, MOST, MIST, BRICK, BOOK
DID YOU FIND ANY OTHERS?

## 235. Crazy cat shadows
a-3
b-2
c-4
d-1

## 236. Dressing up
1 PATTERN ON GIRL'S HAT
2 GIRL'S HAIR
3 COWBOY'S HAT
4 COWBOY'S BADGE
5 COWBOY'S HAIR
6 DOG'S CROWN
7 PATTERN ON JESTER'S HAT
8 JESTER'S SHOES
9 SPOT MISSING FROM NECKERCHIEF
10 FRILL ON JESTER'S TUNIC

## 239. Quiz time
a) its skin tone

## 244. Show-jumping numbers

```
F O R T Y T W O Q
O W E W R Y U T P
U A S E D E G H S
R J X L C I V I E
N Q E V R G T R V
I O P E A H S T E
F I F T Y T F E N
K L B C D E R E W
E I G H T E S N J
A N T W E N T Y K
```

## 245. Puzzle wheel
DONKEY

## 246. Tidied away

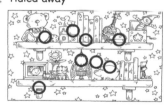

## 248. Muddled story
3 2
4 1

## 249. Ghastly gallery wordsearch

```
H I D E O U S Y S
E V I L N M C X A
L N G O I Y A O D
G H E W G X R G H
A J O S E F Y A A
V M R T L R D S R
P A G E Y H D U R
C D E I O R G E Y
F R A N K I E J X
A Z V J H P V J T
```

**251.** Word trail

Grid:
| K | I | T | E | M | U | M | B | R |
| C | | | | | | | E | E |
| U | | | | | | | L | L |
| D | | | | | | | L | A |
| N | | | | | | | A | L |
| I | | | | | | | R | A |
| W | | | | | | | M | R |
| O | | | | | | | C | M |
| B | | | | | | | L | |
| N | | | | | | | O | |
| I | | | | | | | C | |
| A | | | | | | | K | |
| R | | | | | | | | |
| E | L | I | A | R | T | L | I | K |

**255.** What's gone wrong?

ELEPHANT IN AUDIENCE
JUGGLER WITH ONE SHOE
PINEAPPLE ON RINGMASTER'S HEAD
ONE WHEEL ON SKATEBOARD
FISH BOW TIE

**256.** Sailing numbers

Grid:
```
              N
              I
           T E N
        F     E
      E I G H T
        F     E
      F   T H R E E
    S I X T Y     N
      V         O
  N I N E T E E N
          E
```

**257.** Dinosaur sports day

**258.** Jumble
slippers
surfboard
butterfly
alarm clock

**264.** Puzzle wheel
SATURN

**265.** Hidden word
DOLPHIN

**266.** Puzzle cobweb
WIZARDS

**267.** Magic numbers

```
          S       E
     T H R E E    L
     E       V  T E N
   F I V E   E  L  E
   G       N I N E T E E
   H       I    E  N
   T W E N T Y  N
           E
```

**268.** Word machine
MAD, SAD, MEAN, MEAL,
MEET, SEAT, SEE, SEA, SE
STAND, STEAM, SEAM, TE
DID YOU THINK OF ANY O

**270.** Robotic word puzzles
ROB, RAT, ROOT, RING, RA
TRAIN, TIN, IN, IT, NOT,
COT, COAT
DID YOU THINK OF ANY OT

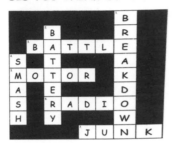

Grid:
```
              B
          B   R
      B A T T L E
  S   T       A
  M O T O R   K
  A   E       D
  S   R A D I O
  H   Y       W
      J U N K
```

**271.** Racing words

```
S M C R U S H B U R
B C L Y R E T T A B
B R M U I H C V G R
U A S R C O R B E O
R S M L N C O A L B
N H L T N O T R T A
A G R A D I O K T K
T O V H S A M S T L
L C R A R A D P B M
H T E A M J S K L X
```

**272.** Word trail

Grid:
| S | O | A | P | A | N | D | A | N |
| G | | | | | | | | T |
| N | | | | | | | | O |
| I | | | | | | | | Y |
| R | | | | | | | | O |
| A | | | | | | | | Y |
| E | | | | | | | | O |
| S | | | | | | | | S |
| U | | | | | | | | T |
| O | | | | | | | | R |
| H | | | | | | | | I |
| T | | | | | | | | C |
| H | | | | | | | | H |
| G | I | L | A | T | I | P | S | O |

**164.** Puzzle wheel
GRAPES
ORANGE

**165.** Quiz time
b) 32

**168.** A giant step

**169.** Questions and answers
1 light
2 rainbow
3 horse
4 rice
5 space shuttle

**170.** Hidden word
OAK

**171.** Word trail

| ¹H | A | M | M | E | ²R | A | F | ³T |
| S | ¹ | | | | 2 | | | R |
| I | ³ | | | 4 | | | | A |
| F | R | | | | | | | ¹N |
| ⁴S | | | | 6 | | | | E |
| E | ⁷ | | | 8 | | | | W |
| V | | | | | | | | S |
| O | ⁹ | | | ¹⁰ | | | | P |
| ⁹G | | | ¹¹ | | | | | ⁶R |
| O | | | | | | | | |
| ⁸D | N | O | P | M | A | ⁷L | I | A |

**172.** Quiz time
a) feathers

**173.** Clever crossword

```
                    19 - 16 =
                         T
        29 - 12 =        H
            S            R
8 + 4 = T W E L V E
            V    4 x 5 = E
25 ÷ 5 = F I V E    T
            N       W
30 - 15 = F I F T E E N
            E       N
            E       T
            N       Y
```

**176.** Jumble scramble
water lily
tractor
seaweed
saxophone

**177.** Quiz time
b) Egypt

**181.** Quiz time
b) an ostrich

**184.** Desert puzzle

| T | F | O | U | R | T | E | E | N |
| H | O | Q | W | E | T | Y | U | I |
| I | R | I | O | P | A | S | D | N |
| R | T | W | E | N | T | Y | X | E |
| Y | Y | F | G | H | J | K | L | T |
| N | T | Z | N | F | I | F | T | Y |
| I | W | C | I | V | B | M | Q | N |
| N | O | W | N | E | R | T | Y | I |
| E | U | I | E | S | E | V | E | N |
| E | A | D | G | J | D | S | B | E |

**185.** Quiz time
b) a giant tortoise

**187.** Potions
heaviest - 2kg of tentacles
lightest - 10kg of frogspawn

**188.** Quiz time
c) bees

**193.** Quiz time
c) every 4 years

**194.** Puzzle cobweb
CAULDRON

**195.** Molehill madness

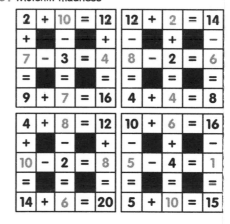

| 2 | + | 10 | = | 12 | | 12 | + | 2 | = | 14 |
| + | | - | | + | | - | | + | | - |
| 7 | - | 3 | = | 4 | | 8 | - | 2 | = | 6 |
| = | | = | | = | | = | | = | | = |
| 9 | + | 7 | = | 16 | | 4 | + | 4 | = | 8 |

| 4 | + | 8 | = | 12 | | 10 | + | 6 | = | 16 |
| + | | - | | + | | - | | + | | - |
| 10 | - | 2 | = | 8 | | 5 | - | 4 | = | 1 |
| = | | = | | = | | = | | = | | = |
| 14 | + | 6 | = | 20 | | 5 | + | 10 | = | 15 |

**198.** Crossword puzzle

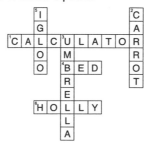

**199.** Quiz time
b) blue whale

**202.** What's gone wrong?
MOUSE FLYING
CHIMNEY IN TREES
DEER WEARING HAT
PENCIL TRUNK
MOLE WEARING GLASSES

**203.** A fairy flit

**206.** Quiz time
b) a limbo

**207.** Questions and answers
1 attic
2 tomorrow
3 butter
4 stallion
5 cook

**208.** Word wizard
FEATHERS

**209.** Formula 1 numbers

**212.** Word trail

**214.** Quiz time
a) in its pouch

**215.** Questions and answers
1 dog
2 stars
3 nanny
4 top
5 wine

**217.** Number squares

| 10 | + | 2 | = | 12 | | 9 | − | 3 | = | 6 |
|----|---|---|---|----|---|---|---|---|---|---|
| + | | | | + | | + | | | | + |
| 7 | − | 2 | = | 5 | | 2 | + | 2 | = | 4 |
| = | | = | | = | | = | | | | = |
| 17 | − | 0 | = | 17 | | 11 | − | 1 | = | 10 |

| 15 | − | 7 | = | 8 | | 7 | + | 3 | = | 10 |
|----|---|---|---|---|---|---|---|---|---|----|
| − | | − | | − | | + | | − | | + |
| 5 | − | 3 | = | 2 | | 7 | − | 2 | = | 5 |
| = | | = | | = | | = | | = | | = |
| 10 | − | 4 | = | 6 | | 14 | + | 1 | = | 15 |

**221.** Coded letter
HELP! NEED TO CAST A SPELL.

**222.** Quiz time
d) to tell other wolves where they are

**223.** Animal magic

| 12 | + | 12 | = | 24 | | 2 | × | 3 | = | 6 |
|----|---|----|---|----|---|---|---|---|---|---|
| − | | − | | − | | × | | × | | × |
| 6 | + | 8 | = | 14 | | 6 | × | 1 | = | 6 |
| = | | = | | = | | = | | = | | = |
| 6 | + | 4 | = | 10 | | 12 | × | 3 | = | 36 |

| 2 | + | 7 | = | 9 | | 10 | − | 5 | = | 5 |
|---|---|---|---|---|---|----|---|---|---|---|
| + | | − | | | | | | + | | − |
| 2 | + | 5 | = | 7 | | 2 | + | 3 | = | 5 |
| = | | = | | = | | = | | | | = |
| 4 | − | 2 | = | 2 | | 8 | − | 8 | = | 0 |

**225.** Word puzzle

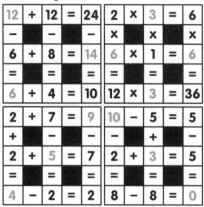

**226.** Robo search

464

**227.** Starting grid

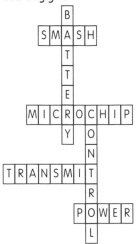

**228.** Crossword puzzle

**229.** Secret postcards
AMERICA
RUSSIA
KENYA

**231.** Find the robots

**232.** Quiz time
c) sting

**233.** Kitten numbers

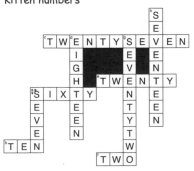

**234.** Word magic
BROOM, STICK, SICK, TICK, ROOM, BOOM, TRICK, IT, MOST, MIST, BRICK, BOOK
DID YOU FIND ANY OTHERS?

**235.** Crazy cat shadows
a-3
b-2
c-4
d-1

**236.** Dressing up
1 PATTERN ON GIRL'S HAT
2 GIRL'S HAIR
3 COWBOY'S HAT
4 COWBOY'S BADGE
5 COWBOY'S HAIR
6 DOG'S CROWN
7 PATTERN ON JESTER'S HAT
8 JESTER'S SHOES
9 SPOT MISSING FROM NECKERCHIEF
10 FRILL ON JESTER'S TUNIC

**239.** Quiz time
a) its skin tone

**244.** Show-jumping numbers

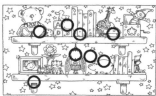

**245.** Puzzle wheel
DONKEY

**246.** Tidied away

**248.** Muddled story
3 2
4 1

**249.** Ghastly gallery wordsearch

## 251. Word trail

| ¹K | I | ²T | E | ³M | U | M | B | R |
|---|---|---|---|---|---|---|---|---|
| C |  | | | | | | | E |
| U | | | | | | | | L |
| ⁹D | | | | | | | | L |
| N | | | | | | | | A |
| I | | | | | | | | L |
| ⁸W | | | | | | | | A |
| O | | | | | | | | R |
| B | | | | | | | | M |
| N | | | | | | | | C |
| I | | | | | | | | L |
| ⁷R | | | | | | | | O |
| E | L | I | A | R | T | L | I | ⁶K |

## 255. What's gone wrong?

ELEPHANT IN AUDIENCE
JUGGLER WITH ONE SHOE
PINEAPPLE ON RINGMASTER'S HEAD
ONE WHEEL ON SKATEBOARD
FISH BOW TIE

## 256. Sailing numbers

| | | | | ¹N | |
|---|---|---|---|---|---|
| | | | | I | |
| | | ⁹T | E | N | |
| | ᶜF | | | E | |
| | ᵈE | I | G | H | T |
| | F | | | T | |
| ᵃF | | ⁷T | H | R | E | E |
| ᵇS | I | X | T | Y | |
| | V | | | ʰO | |
| ⁱN | I | N | E | T | E | E | N |
| | | | | E | |

## 257. Dinosaur sports day

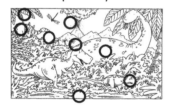

## 258. Jumble

slippers
surfboard
butterfly
alarm clock

## 264. Puzzle wheel

SATURN

## 265. Hidden word

DOLPHIN

## 266. Puzzle cobweb

WIZARDS

## 267. Magic numbers

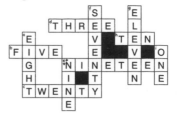

## 268. Word machine

MAD, SAD, MEAN, MEAL, MESS, DAMN, MEAT,
MEET, SEAT, SEE, SEA, SEAL, LEAST, LESS, DEAL,
STAND, STEAM, SEAM, TEAM
DID YOU THINK OF ANY OTHERS?

## 270. Robotic word puzzles

ROB, RAT, ROOT, RING, RAIN, BOOT, BOA, BANG,
TRAIN, TIN, IN, IT, NOT, GRIN, GAIN, GOT, CAR,
COT, COAT
DID YOU THINK OF ANY OTHERS?

## 271. Racing words

| S | M | C | R | U | S | H | B | U | R |
|---|---|---|---|---|---|---|---|---|---|
| B | C | L | Y | R | E | T | T | A | B |
| B | R | M | U | I | H | C | V | G | R |
| A | S | R | C | O | R | B | E | O | O |
| N | M | L | N | C | O | A | L | B | A |
| H | L | T | N | O | T | R | T | A | K |
| A | G | R | A | D | I | O | K | T | K |
| T | O | V | H | S | A | M | S | A | L |
| L | C | R | A | R | A | D | P | B | M |
| H | T | E | A | M | J | S | K | L | X |

## 272. Word trail

| ¹S | O | A | ²P | A | N | D | ³A | N |
|---|---|---|---|---|---|---|---|---|
| G | | | | | | | | ⁴T |
| N | | | | | | | | ⁵O |
| ¹⁰R | | | | | | | | Y |
| ⁹E | | | | | | | | ⁶O |
| U | | | | | | | | S |
| ⁸O | | | | | | | | T |
| H | | | | | | | | R |
| T | | | | | | | | I |
| H | | | | | | | | C |
| G | I | ⁸L | A | T | I | P | S | ⁷O |

## 273. Plant spotting

```
J R E I T U L I P
R O S E L K B Y A
I O D N P L W C R
K X H Q A R G A S
C R E F N P Z C L
H D A I S Y H T E
D U T M Y L W U Y
R K H B U T U S Q
O T E S K Q Z Y D
M A R I G O L D G
```

## 274. Junk box

```
T L O B E C R R A C
C H A I N I R G N E
R X Y V G G B L M B
A P W S I T M O N P
N R H T N N U O A R
E X E R E L O N P T
S T E X V B P A R S
O A L R I L R U Y T
X P V K T Q C M G V
S T E E K K S N V X
```

## 275. Questions and answers
1 stop
2 sheep
3 breakfast
4 purr
5 snail

## 277. Number fun

| 14 | − | 6 | = | 8 |   | 18 | − | 2 | = | 16 |
|----|---|---|---|---|---|----|---|---|---|----|
| −  |   | + |   | − |   | −  |   | + |   | −  |
| 2  | + | 4 | = | 6 |   | 4  | + | 2 | = | 6  |
| =  |   | = |   | = |   | =  |   | = |   | =  |
| 12 | − | 10| = | 2 |   | 14 | − | 4 | = | 10 |

| 16 | − | 3 | = | 13 |   | 3  | + | 7 | = | 10 |
|----|---|---|---|----|---|----|---|---|---|----|
| −  |   | + |   | +  |   | +  |   | − |   | +  |
| 10 | − | 7 | = | 3  |   | 8  | − | 3 | = | 5  |
| =  |   | = |   | =  |   | =  |   | = |   | =  |
| 6  | + | 10| = | 16 |   | 11 | + | 4 | = | 15 |

## 279. Quiz time
c) hibernate

## 280. Words within words
FLOW LOW FLOWER OWE
SWEET CORN
GRAPE FRUIT APE IT TAPE TAP
WATER MELON ATE ON TERM ME
PINE APPLE IN PIN
DID YOU FIND ANY OTHERS?

## 281. Charging station
A-2
B-4
C-1
D-3

## 282. Jumble
fire place
accordion
boomerang
ghost

## 283. Quiz time
d) a meteorologist

## 284. Tree puzzles

| 3  | + | 2 | = | 5  |   | 2  | x | 3 | = | 6  |
|----|---|---|---|----|---|----|---|---|---|----|
| +  |   | − |   | +  |   | x  |   | x |   | x  |
| 9  | − | 1 | = | 8  |   | 6  | x | 1 | = | 6  |
| =  |   | = |   | =  |   | =  |   | = |   | =  |
| 12 | + | 1 | = | 13 |   | 12 | x | 3 | = | 36 |

| 12 | + | 12 | = | 24 |   | 11 | − | 4 | = | 7  |
|----|---|----|---|----|---|----|---|---|---|----|
| −  |   | −  |   | −  |   | +  |   | − |   | +  |
| 6  | + | 8  | = | 14 |   | 5  | + | 2 | = | 7  |
| =  |   | =  |   | =  |   | =  |   | = |   | =  |
| 6  | + | 4  | = | 10 |   | 16 | − | 2 | = | 14 |

## 285. Spooky numbers
5 + 3 = 8
6 - 5 = 1
4 + 8 = 12
8 - 7 = 1
3 + 9 = 12

## 287. Afternoon nap

## 289. Word puzzles
battery

1 DARK
2 YANK
3 DAY
4 JAR
5 RAY

## 290. Quiz time
a) Japan

## 291. Cheesy numbers

| 5 | + | 7  | = | 12 |   | 5  | + | 6 | = | 11 |
|---|---|----|---|----|---|----|---|---|---|----|
| + |   | +  |   | +  |   | +  |   | − |   | +  |
| 4 | + | 5  | = | 9  |   | 7  | − | 4 | = | 3  |
| = |   | =  |   | =  |   | =  |   | = |   | =  |
| 9 | + | 12 | = | 21 |   | 12 | + | 2 | = | 14 |

| 6  | + | 8 | = | 14 |   | 8  | + | 2 | = | 10 |
|----|---|---|---|----|---|----|---|---|---|----|
| +  |   | − |   | +  |   | +  |   | − |   | +  |
| 6  | − | 4 | = | 2  |   | 8  | − | 2 | = | 6  |
| =  |   | = |   | =  |   | =  |   | = |   | =  |
| 12 | + | 4 | = | 16 |   | 16 | + | 0 | = | 16 |

293. Pet spotting

```
R B C A N A R Y S
A W A Q Y G J F B
B I T A M O U S E
B R D C S L K L E
I R W V Z D O G V
T H L J S F T O D
Q Y R B C I D X P
U B H A M S T E R
H V M T S H S O A
P O N Y E Y E O M
```

294. Animals crossword

```
        B
        E
        A
  C R O C O D I L E
  A     O
  M   P A N D A
  E     K
  L I O N E
        Y
```

295. Food search

```
J S E E R Z U H M
C K R A M E Q P O
H C M L H O N E Y
E G G K E U Y T E
R S P C W X B H T
R M B H Q R U L O
I N V E T F R I P
E I J E Y R G F H
S A U S A G E S U
S D O E H Y R P Q
```

296. Happy Humpty

297. Quiz time
b) the neck feathers

301. Word puzzles

```
      S E A T
      P     O
  S C R A P  O
  C   N     L
  R   N
  E   W E L D
  W   R   R
      W I R E
      V
      M E T A L
```

1 RAT
2 BOAT
3 RING
4 ROAR
5 BRAIN

303. Quiz time
c) ostrich

304. Disco numbers

```
  F I F T E E N
    O
  T H I R T Y
  W     T
  T W E N T Y F I V E
  N     N       L
  T W E L V E   E
  Y     I       V
  O     G       E
  N     H   T E N
  E     T
        Y
```

305. Spy's word puzzle

```
M J S O R H P I B
I O C P S I H K I
C A M E R A U L N
R Z Q N Y T Q B O
O B N C V S E G C
P M S I L P E Y U
H X T L O Y R M L
O J Y W A B U O A
N O T E P A D R R
E K R A M Q J B S
```

306. Prehistoric times
WHAT IS A
TYRANNOSAURUS REX?

310. Quiz time
d) Germany

311. Alien encounter

312. Circuit breaker
C

313. Word trail

```
E A R I N G R A P
S             P E
R             S
U             N
N             O W
R             W
O             M
C             A N
A             E
D             S
N             T
A             E
M L I A T O P A
```

314. Junkyard jumbles

Pick a spanner
C F B D E A

Cog question
16

Lost letters
METAL

316. Festive numbers

| T | W | E | N | T | Y | O | N | E |
|---|---|---|---|---|---|---|---|---|
| W | A | V | B | W | L | C | M | I |
| E | N | D | X | O | E | W | P | G |
| N | F | Q | G | Y | H | Z | I | H |
| T | J | S | I | X | T | Y | K | T |
| Y | L | A | M | R | B | N | S | C |
| F | O | R | T | Y | T | W | O | F |
| I | O | D | P | F | Q | E | R | I |
| V | G | T | W | E | L | V | E | V |
| E | S | H | J | T | I | U | K | E |

317. Quiz time
a) Black

318. Whose house?
a-4
b-3
c-1
d-2

319. Spell casting
1 CAT'S WHISKERS MISSING
2 BOOKMARK
3 FOOT ON CAULDRON MISSING
4 LABEL ON BOTTLE MISSING
5 DRAWER HANDLE MISSING
6 MOON MISSING FROM CLOAK
7 BAND ON WITCH'S HAT
8 WIZARD'S FOOT MISSING
9 ANOTHER DRAWER HANDLE MISSING
10 WITCH'S TOOTH MISSING
11 BUBBLE IN FLASK MISSING

320. Sounds good!

TRIANGLE

321. Toot toot!

322. Mystery maze
pineapple

323. Quiz time
a) laughing

327. What's gone wrong?
KITE   WITH   BALLOONS
OWL ON CLOWN'S HEAD
SOCK ON TABLE
SNAILS ON TABLE
CAT SAT AT TABLE

328. Word web
WIZARD

331. Crossword puzzle

332. One out of two
PAN  -  CAKE
COW  -  BOY
FIRE  -  MAN
STEP  -  LADDER

334. Puzzle wheel
VIOLET
THOMAS

335. Clothes search

| G | K | S | W | E | E | L | M | O |
|---|---|---|---|---|---|---|---|---|
| S | R | O | X | U | K | M | D | O |
| H | A | T | G | S | O | C | K | S |
| I | M | W | P | H | I | V | Z | A |
| R | F | B | M | O | N | O | P | D |
| T | E | I | Z | E | X | H | O | D |
| A | L | L | T | S | U | S | S | R |
| E | D | Y | I | Q | E | T | I | E |
| H | O | Z | C | M | Q | U | P | S |
| S | J | E | A | N | S | E | R | S |

337. First letters
SECRET

338. Nature watch

| P | S | N | A | I | L | Q | E | R |
|---|---|---|---|---|---|---|---|---|
| A | D | G | H | C | E | J | K | Z |
| E | T | Y | D | J | A | F | N | E |
| S | B | W | R | I | F | K | G | K |
| H | P | H | U | Q | N | B | H | R |
| E | U | X | L | N | Q | R | S | A |
| D | T | I | H | E | W | X | E | M |
| D | V | L | Z | E | B | D | F | J |
| S | L | B | O | G | T | W | Y | G | J |
| U | G | C | U | K | B | I | R | D |

**339.** Muddled machine
1 6
2 EVEREST
3 CANADA
4 DODO
5 T-REX
6 PARIS
7 12 O'CLOCK
8 SLEEPING

**340/341.** Hidden wands
15

**342.** Hidden word
JAMES

**343.** Word trail

**346.** Number puzzle

| 7 | + | 3 | = | 10 |
|---|---|---|---|---|
| − | | − | | − |
| 2 | + | 0 | = | 2 |
| = | | = | | = |
| 5 | + | 3 | = | 8 |

**347.** Telephone differences
1 TAIL MISSING FROM CAT
2 WIRING DIFFERENT
3 LAPEL MISSING
4 EARPIECE MISSING
5 PART OF CLOAK MISSING
6 HAND MISSING

**348.** Most and least
THE WIZARD HAS THE MOST-13
THE WITCH HAS THE FEWEST-12

**350.** Quiz time
d) South Africa

**352.** Shadow search
C

**353.** How many squares?
13

**354.** Program puzzle
ROBOT RACING RULES
MACHINE MAYHEM
ROBOBEAST DANGER
JUNKYARD BATTLE

**356.** In the city

**357.** Do you know?
1 PEN
2 OPEN
3 LEAVES
4 HIVE

**358.** Quiz time
a) sharks

**359.** Puzzle cobweb
POTION

**360.** Welcome robots

**362.** Number sudoku

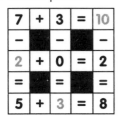

**364.** Odd bot out
D

**365.** Quiz time
b) a butterfly

**366.** Marine garden

**367.** Kitten capers
KITTENS LIKE TO DRINK MILK AND PLAY WITH
BALLS OF WOOL.

**368.** Pattern sudoku

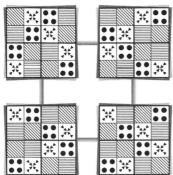

**370.** Roald Dahl story search

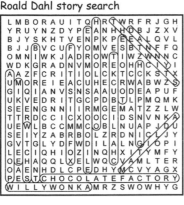

**371.** Treasure island

SKULL MOUNTAIN
SCALP CORNER
FIRE ISLAND
ALLIGATOR ALLEY
BANANA BUNCH
GORILLA GROVE

**372.** Quiz time

c) cheetah

**373.** King of the castle

**374.** Where and when?

THESE CHILDREN ARE MEETING UNDER THE CLOCK
AT TWO O'CLOCK.

**375.** Animal sudoku

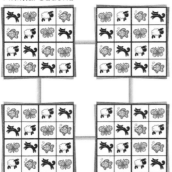

**376.** Crossed words

**377.** Twice the fun

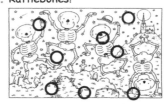

BUCKET

**378.** Rattlebones!

**379.** Picture search

| B | C | H | C | G | E | N | T | U | T |
|---|---|---|---|---|---|---|---|---|---|
| O | O | A | I | H | G | H | I | U | X |
| L | S | L | N | F | A | B | I | N | N |
| R | P | E | T | N | A | I | G | S | P |
| E | A | W | H | E | E | L | N | E | Q |
| N | N | S | P | A | N | C | F | A | R |
| N | P | Y | D | E | P | E | R | T | S |
| A | Y | Y | D | T | E | R | S | U | P |
| P | B | E | N | G | I | N | E | P | J |
| S | O | N | U | K | P | A | R | G | L |

**380.** Quiz time

d) tiger

**381.** Disguises

| M | C | A | F | H | A | T | Q | J |
|---|---|---|---|---|---|---|---|---|
| A | P | W | B | S | B | K | G | L |
| G | L | A | R | O | D | Y | L | I |
| N | F | Z | I | Q | C | O | A | T |
| I | R | G | E | G | Q | R | S | O |
| F | V | E | F | A | U | G | S | G |
| Y | R | B | C | K | H | L | E | L |
| I | R | L | A | S | P | D | S | A |
| N | Q | N | S | K | R | A | M | S |
| G | C | B | E | A | R | D | X | S |

### 382. Animal sudoku

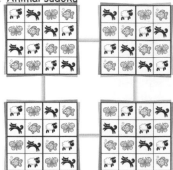

### 383. Underwater search

### 384. Tell the time
**WHAT TIME IS MIDDAY?**

### 385. Number puzzle

| 2 | + | 8 | = | 10 |
|---|---|---|---|----|
| − |   | − |   | −  |
| 1 | + | 2 | = | 3  |
| = |   | = |   | =  |
| 1 | + | 6 | = | 7  |

### 388. Quiz time
b) 2

### 389. Two into one
FOOT - BALL
DOOR - BELL
STAR - FISH
EAR - DRUM

### 390. Shadow search
D

### 391. Nuts and Bolts
42 NUTS
30 BOLTS

### 392. Number sudoku

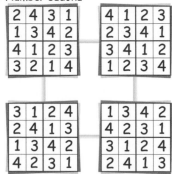

### 393. In search of numbers

### 395. Quiz time
a) dams

### 396. Washed and ready

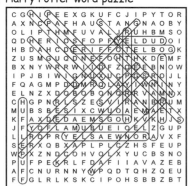

### 398. Pick 'em up
four spanners

### 399. Quiz time
b) 6

### 400. Harry Potter word puzzle

## 401. Letter sudoku

| A | X | M | G |
|---|---|---|---|
| G | M | X | A |
| M | A | G | X |
| X | G | A | M |

| X | A | M | G |
|---|---|---|---|
| G | M | A | X |
| M | X | G | A |
| A | G | X | M |

| M | X | G | A |
|---|---|---|---|
| A | G | X | M |
| X | A | M | G |
| G | M | A | X |

| G | X | A | M |
|---|---|---|---|
| M | A | G | X |
| A | M | X | G |
| X | G | M | A |

## 402. In a jam

MOUSE BALANCING BALL ON ITS NOSE
CAT DRIVING CAR
GIRAFFE STICKING HEAD OUT OF CAR
WHEEL MISSING
MAN DRIVING ON BACK OF CAR

## 403. Sudoku

| 1 | 9 | 3 | 7 | 8 | 2 | 5 | 4 | 6 |
|---|---|---|---|---|---|---|---|---|
| 2 | 5 | 6 | 9 | 3 | 4 | 1 | 8 | 7 |
| 8 | 4 | 7 | 5 | 6 | 1 | 3 | 9 | 2 |
| 7 | 1 | 9 | 6 | 2 | 8 | 4 | 5 | 3 |
| 3 | 6 | 5 | 1 | 4 | 9 | 7 | 2 | 8 |
| 4 | 8 | 2 | 3 | 7 | 5 | 6 | 1 | 9 |
| 6 | 2 | 4 | 8 | 5 | 7 | 9 | 3 | 1 |
| 5 | 7 | 1 | 2 | 9 | 3 | 8 | 6 | 4 |
| 9 | 3 | 8 | 4 | 1 | 6 | 2 | 7 | 5 |

## 404. Sports crossword

```
    S
    W   2
    I   S U R F I N G
    M   K
3 G Y M N A S T I C S
    M       E   Y
    I       N   C
    N       N   L
    G       I   I
            S   N
                G
```

## 405. Picture sudoku

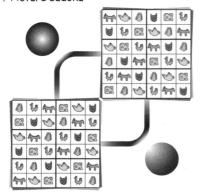

## 408. Sudoku

| 9 | 1 | 3 | 6 | 5 | 8 | 7 | 4 | 2 |
|---|---|---|---|---|---|---|---|---|
| 5 | 4 | 2 | 1 | 3 | 7 | 6 | 8 | 9 |
| 8 | 7 | 6 | 9 | 4 | 2 | 5 | 1 | 3 |
| 4 | 2 | 1 | 7 | 8 | 5 | 3 | 9 | 6 |
| 6 | 5 | 7 | 3 | 1 | 9 | 8 | 2 | 4 |
| 3 | 9 | 8 | 4 | 2 | 6 | 1 | 5 | 7 |
| 2 | 3 | 4 | 8 | 7 | 1 | 9 | 6 | 5 |
| 7 | 8 | 9 | 5 | 6 | 4 | 2 | 3 | 1 |
| 1 | 6 | 5 | 2 | 9 | 3 | 4 | 7 | 8 |

## 409. Family word puzzle

```
P X A W B M O T H E R Y P Y G
H Y B N I S U O C H H X M D T
B P J R Y H H K E I B S Y O P
N V Y R R N M Q A G Y C L I V
W X G Y A E B A R W E H P E N
Q W I N T L O A U N J T Q Z A
N T N D H O N X Z A L U Q B N
A A W L S D P E U H U X R R Q
F C T I A V W E J Z Z N S Z N
A Y A D B R O T H E R I T I X
T Z H M N U Q C D B S W E I P
H U X A X U N V U T C C O R E
E B A B Y E N C E P E Q P J V
R W N L N O A R L K C E Z K M
P Q M R L U E V C E A O D P U
```

## 410. Pretty puzzle

| 3 | + | 6 | = | 9 |
|---|---|---|---|---|
| + |   | − |   | − |
| 2 | + | 4 | = | 6 |
| = |   | = |   | = |
| 5 | − | 2 | = | 3 |

## 411. In good shape!

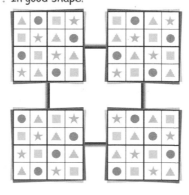

## 412. Eye spy

BAT  BALL  BASKET  BREAD  BOOK  BOTTLE
BUTTERFLIES  BIRD  BOW  BEES  BANANAS
BARK  BUSH  BUTTER
DID YOU FIND ANY OTHERS?

**414.** Count on me!

| 1 | 4 | 2 | 6 | 5 | 3 |
|---|---|---|---|---|---|
| 3 | 6 | 5 | 1 | 4 | 2 |
| 4 | 5 | 1 | 3 | 2 | 6 |
| 2 | 3 | 6 | 5 | 1 | 4 |
| 5 | 2 | 3 | 4 | 6 | 1 |
| 6 | 1 | 4 | 2 | 3 | 5 |

| 5 | 2 | 3 | 4 | 6 | 1 |
|---|---|---|---|---|---|
| 6 | 1 | 4 | 2 | 3 | 5 |
| 2 | 3 | 6 | 5 | 1 | 4 |
| 4 | 5 | 1 | 3 | 2 | 6 |
| 3 | 6 | 5 | 1 | 4 | 2 |
| 1 | 4 | 2 | 6 | 5 | 3 |

**415.** Which one?
C

**416.** Picture sudoku

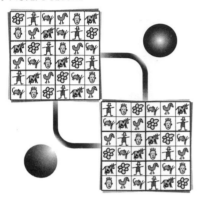

**418.** Problem puzzle

| 15 | − | 5 | = | 10 |
|----|---|---|---|----|
| −  |   | − |   | −  |
| 11 | − | 4 | = | 7  |
| =  |   | = |   | =  |
| 4  | − | 1 | = | 3  |

**419.** Picture sudoku

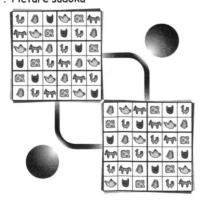
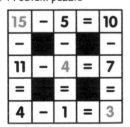

**420.** Weather report!

THUNDER

**421.** Crossword challenge

| E | S | C | A | P | E |   | B | A | R | B | E | R |
|---|---|---|---|---|---|---|---|---|---|---|---|---|
| N |   | A |   | L |   | R |   | L |   | R |   | I |
| M | A | N | D | A | T | E |   | I | L | I | A | D |
| I |   | O |   | T |   | N |   | B |   | T |   | E |
| T | A | N | G | O |   | A | V | I | A | T | O | R |
| Y |   | O |   | I |   | I |   | L |   | S |   | S |
|   | B | U | E | N | O | S | A | I | R | E | S |   |
| F |   | N |   | S |   | N |   | N |   |   |   | G |
| A | M | N | E | S | I | A |   | P | I | S | T | E |
| T |   | E |   | T |   | N |   | R |   | E |   | C |
| C | A | R | G | O |   | C | H | I | N | O | O | K |
| A |   | V |   | N |   | E |   | U |   | N |   | O |
| T | H | E | B | E | S |   | S | T | I | L | T | S |

**422.** Number sudoku

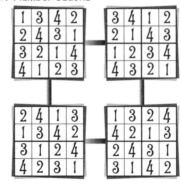

| 1 | 3 | 4 | 2 |
|---|---|---|---|
| 2 | 4 | 3 | 1 |
| 3 | 2 | 1 | 4 |
| 4 | 1 | 2 | 3 |

| 3 | 4 | 1 | 2 |
|---|---|---|---|
| 2 | 1 | 4 | 3 |
| 1 | 2 | 3 | 4 |
| 4 | 3 | 2 | 1 |

| 2 | 4 | 1 | 3 |
|---|---|---|---|
| 1 | 3 | 4 | 2 |
| 3 | 1 | 2 | 4 |
| 4 | 2 | 3 | 1 |

| 1 | 3 | 2 | 4 |
|---|---|---|---|
| 4 | 2 | 1 | 3 |
| 2 | 4 | 3 | 1 |
| 3 | 1 | 4 | 2 |

**423.** Present time!
PAIR OF GLASSES
PINEAPPLE
TOY TRAIN
DUCK

**424.** Six in a fix!

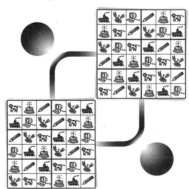

**26. Pattern puzzler**

**433. Letter sudoku**

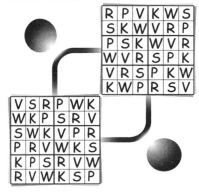

**27. Bird word puzzle**

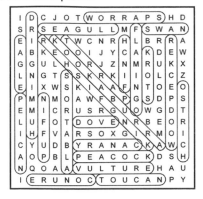

**434. Missing letters**

JAMES LOUISE
MARIA MARK

**435. Sudoku**

| 4 | 7 | 8 | 3 | 1 | 6 | 5 | 2 | 9 |
|---|---|---|---|---|---|---|---|---|
| 6 | 9 | 5 | 8 | 2 | 7 | 1 | 4 | 3 |
| 3 | 1 | 2 | 5 | 4 | 9 | 7 | 8 | 6 |
| 5 | 6 | 1 | 9 | 8 | 3 | 4 | 7 | 2 |
| 8 | 4 | 9 | 1 | 7 | 2 | 6 | 3 | 5 |
| 7 | 2 | 3 | 6 | 5 | 4 | 8 | 9 | 1 |
| 1 | 8 | 4 | 2 | 3 | 5 | 9 | 6 | 7 |
| 9 | 3 | 7 | 4 | 6 | 1 | 2 | 5 | 8 |
| 2 | 5 | 6 | 7 | 9 | 8 | 3 | 1 | 4 |

**430. Pick a picture**

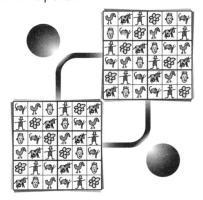

**438. Shaping up!**

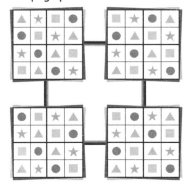

**431. Character word puzzle**

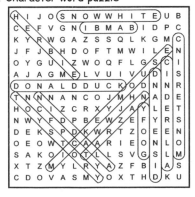

**439. Don't be late!**

SPY MEETING AT MIDDAY

**440. Camping word puzzle**

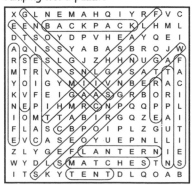

**443.** Sudoku

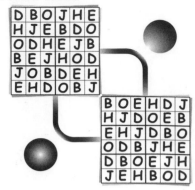

| 4 | 8 | 2 | 5 | 9 | 1 | 6 | 3 | 7 |
|---|---|---|---|---|---|---|---|---|
| 3 | 9 | 1 | 4 | 6 | 7 | 5 | 8 | 2 |
| 7 | 5 | 6 | 3 | 2 | 8 | 9 | 4 | 1 |
| 2 | 7 | 3 | 6 | 4 | 5 | 1 | 9 | 8 |
| 5 | 6 | 9 | 1 | 8 | 3 | 2 | 7 | 4 |
| 8 | 1 | 4 | 2 | 7 | 9 | 3 | 5 | 6 |
| 9 | 4 | 5 | 7 | 1 | 6 | 8 | 2 | 3 |
| 6 | 3 | 7 | 8 | 5 | 2 | 4 | 1 | 9 |
| 1 | 2 | 8 | 9 | 3 | 4 | 7 | 6 | 5 |

**444.** Library spy

BOOK MISSING TOP LEFT
END OF GIRL'S HAIR BUNCH
BOOK MISSING RIGHT OF GIRL
EYE MISSING
POCKET MISSING
BIRD'S TELESCOPE MISSING
HAT MISSING
FACE BETWEEN BOOKS MISSING

**445.** Pattern sudoku

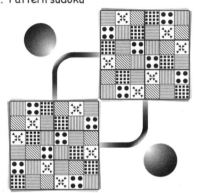

**447.** Number rumba

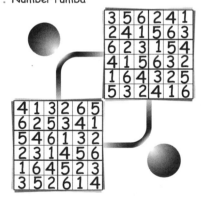

| 3 | 5 | 6 | 2 | 4 | 1 |
|---|---|---|---|---|---|
| 2 | 4 | 1 | 5 | 6 | 3 |
| 6 | 2 | 3 | 1 | 5 | 4 |
| 4 | 1 | 5 | 6 | 3 | 2 |
| 1 | 6 | 4 | 3 | 2 | 5 |
| 5 | 3 | 2 | 4 | 1 | 6 |

| 4 | 1 | 3 | 2 | 6 | 5 |
|---|---|---|---|---|---|
| 6 | 2 | 5 | 3 | 4 | 1 |
| 5 | 4 | 6 | 1 | 3 | 2 |
| 2 | 3 | 1 | 4 | 5 | 6 |
| 1 | 6 | 4 | 5 | 2 | 3 |
| 3 | 5 | 2 | 6 | 1 | 4 |

**449.** Shopping word puzzle

| N | M | F | H | I | R | Y | O | Y |
|---|---|---|---|---|---|---|---|---|
| D | E | S | H | A | M | P | O | O |
| R | E | N | L | P | W | Q | C | G |
| F | S | O | A | P | K | L | D | H |
| B | G | U | R | L | P | C | Z | U |
| U | S | F | B | E | H | H | M | R |
| T | R | I | Y | S | U | E | C | T |
| T | L | S | O | W | Q | E | R | E |
| E | J | H | Q | I | U | S | F | E |
| R | K | F | D | B | R | E | A | D |

**450.** Letter sudoku

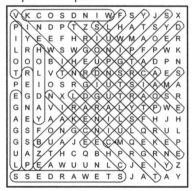

| D | B | O | J | H | E |
|---|---|---|---|---|---|
| H | J | E | B | D | O |
| O | D | H | E | J | B |
| B | E | J | H | O | D |
| J | O | B | D | E | H |
| E | H | D | O | B | J |

| B | O | E | H | D | J |
|---|---|---|---|---|---|
| H | J | D | O | E | B |
| E | H | J | D | B | O |
| O | D | B | J | H | E |
| D | B | O | E | J | H |
| J | E | H | B | O | D |

**451.** Sudoku

| 6 | 3 | 9 | 8 | 2 | 5 | 4 | 1 | 7 |
|---|---|---|---|---|---|---|---|---|
| 8 | 1 | 2 | 3 | 7 | 4 | 9 | 5 | 6 |
| 4 | 5 | 7 | 9 | 6 | 1 | 3 | 8 | 2 |
| 9 | 6 | 5 | 1 | 4 | 2 | 7 | 3 | 8 |
| 7 | 4 | 8 | 6 | 9 | 3 | 5 | 2 | 1 |
| 1 | 2 | 3 | 7 | 5 | 8 | 6 | 9 | 4 |
| 5 | 9 | 6 | 2 | 1 | 7 | 8 | 4 | 3 |
| 3 | 7 | 1 | 4 | 8 | 9 | 2 | 6 | 5 |
| 2 | 8 | 4 | 5 | 3 | 6 | 1 | 7 | 9 |

**452.** Airport word puzzle

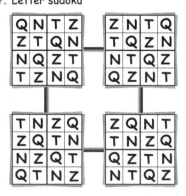

| V | K | C | O | S | D | N | I | W | F | S | Y | J | S | X |
|---|---|---|---|---|---|---|---|---|---|---|---|---|---|---|
| P | I | N | D | P | T | Z | S | L | H | A | T | S | Y | D |
| I | Y | E | E | F | H | R | I | U | W | M | A | O | E | R |
| L | R | H | W | S | W | G | O | N | I | P | F | P | W | K |
| O | T | O | O | B | I | H | E | U | P | G | T | A | D | P | N |
| T | R | O | L | I | V | T | N | R | D | N | S | R | C | A | E | S |
| E | E | L | O | S | R | G | I | U | T | S | I | X | A | M | A |
| G | N | D | N | X | L | D | G | U | T | R | A | O | S | R |
| A | E | A | V | I | R | A | R | A | L | Y | T | P | W | E |
| A | Y | A | A | K | E | N | I | L | S | F | H | J | H |
| G | S | F | O | N | G | C | N | I | U | L | Q | R | U | L |
| U | A | Z | T | H | C | Q | B | H | P | R | G | R | N | E |
| L | P | E | A | W | U | U | N | L | C | J | E | I | Y | Z |
| S | S | E | D | R | A | W | E | T | S | J | A | T | A | Y |

**454.** Letter sudoku

| Q | N | T | Z |
|---|---|---|---|
| Z | T | Q | N |
| N | Q | Z | T |
| T | Z | N | Q |

| Z | N | T | Q |
|---|---|---|---|
| T | Q | Z | N |
| N | T | Q | Z |
| Q | Z | N | T |

| T | N | Z | Q |
|---|---|---|---|
| Z | Q | T | N |
| N | Z | Q | T |
| Q | T | N | Z |

| Z | Q | N | T |
|---|---|---|---|
| T | N | Z | Q |
| N | Z | Q | T |
| Q | Z | T | N |

**456.** Awesome anagrams

hippopotamus
binoculars
telephone
wizard